THE 2ND NEW GRAB A PENCIL® BOOK OF SEEK-A-WORD

RICHARD MANCHESTER

BRISTOL PARK BOOKS
NEW YORK

First Bristol Park Books edition published in 2000.

Bristol Park Books
A division of BBS Publishing Corporation
386 Park Avenue South
New York, NY 10016

Bristol Park Books is a registered trademark of BBS Publishing Corporation.

"Grab a Pencil" is a registered trademark of BBS Publishing Corporation.

Published by arrangement with Crosstown Publications.

ISBN: 0-88486-263-1

Printed in the United States of America.

Contents

Puzzles

RELATIVITY

The 36 famous people in the Word List are all distant relatives of the same person. Once you've found them all in the diagram, adding the correct missing letters, the letters will spell out the name of the mystery relative. Can you do it?

AGA KHAN
ALCOTT (Louisa May)
AUSTEN (Jane)
BISMARCK (Otto von)
BOGART (Humphrey)
BRADLEE (Ben)
CATHERINE (the Great)
CHURCHILL (Sir Winston)
COOLIDGE (Calvin)
CROMWELL (Oliver)
DE HAVILLAND (Olivia)
DE SADE (Marquis)
D'ESTAING
  (Valery Giscard)
DOUGLAS-HOME (Sir
  Alec)
EMERSON (Ralph
  Waldo)
F.D.R.
FRASER (Lady Antonia)
GARDNER (Erle Stanley)
GISH (Lillian)
GOERING (Hermann)
GOETHE (Johann von)
GREENE (Graham)
HUNT (Nelson Bunker)
JUAN CARLOS (King)
LAWRENCE (of Arabia)
LUCAN (Lord)
ORWELL (George)
PEPYS (Samuel)
REMICK (Lee)
RUSSELL (Bertrand)
SAND (George)
SARGENT (John Singer)
STOWE (Harriet Beecher)
VANDERBILT (Gloria)
WASHINGTON
  (George)
WOOLF (Virginia)

```
D N A L L I V A H E D K A R
L R E N I R E H T A C L D A
C H U R C H I L L I R F E A
S D I S L L E W M O R C G V
O S D E S A D E O A C A T A
L A G N Y E R N S O K T U N
R A C O P G L E O H L S O D
A D W S E A R L A U T F U E
C O S R [ ] [ ] [ ] [ ] [ ] I R
N U N E E [ ] [ ] [ ] A U K B
A G S M G N N N N R B L C I
U L O E F E C D G P O L R L
J A C W G R E E N E G E A T
R S N O T G N I H S A W M N
I H N T T T C T E C R R S U
H O S S A T E R L E T O I H
S M W I I O E E L D A R B F
E E L A G N I A T S E D D Y
```

The solution and mystery person are on page 90.

SWEET STEEPLES

The Word List below tells the story of one man's fulfilling (and filling!) hobby—munchable models that are in good taste and that taste good. Words grouped together in the Word List will be found together in the diagram.

Peter
Stallmach
of Red
Bank,
New Jersey,
has been
creating
gingerbread
replicas
of famous
churches at
Christmas-
time
for the
last
twenty-
eight
years.
His models,
four feet
high
and three
feet
wide,
include
St. Patrick's
Cathedral
in New
York
and the
Basilica in
Moscow's
Red Square.
He uses
sugar
and spice
to build
something
nice!

```
D Q K G I N G E R B R E A D O
E L Z N E E B S A H N R T Q F
R D I H R Q Z S Z E S A I T F
F T I U K E I H W Q W U M E A
O G H W B L T J E Q O Q E E M
H K Z G I O E E S U C S C F O
H S K C I R T A P T S D I R U
Q C A R S E C Z A Z O E P U S
G I A E O I T S A L M R S O L
N E Y M L Y E A R S E Q D F E
I Q H P L H E E R H T D N A D
T Z E T C L F O R T H E A E O
A R Q R D S A M T S I R H C M
E D U L C N I T W E N T Y I S
R H K Z K N A B S U G A R N I
C A T H E D R A L W E N N I H
```

The solution is on page 81.

4

```
1  9  9  5  7  9  8  8  8  9  3
3  8  0  7  1  4  3  9  9  0  3
5  2  1  8  6  2  3  5  5  2  0
5  1  8  0  6  0  1  3  3  1  4
0  9  3  9  6  8  8  4  8  3  8
3  3  8  2  0  2  6  8  0  2  5
1  4  0  7  7  0  0  2  7  3  8
7  6  9  1  9  3  7  1  9  3  2
6  0  0  3  9  9  0  8  3  0  9
0  1  2  0  3  2  0  3  0  0  7
1  8  3  1  5  8  2  1  1  8  5
```

The solution is on page 81.

HIDDEN NUMBERS

The 24 number combinations in the list are hidden in the diagram horizontally, vertically or diagonally in a straight, unbroken line of digits that read forward or backward. To start you off, 5399 is circled.

4032	6432
4033	6439
4208	6602
4298	6607
5132	7601
5138	7608
5398	7700
5399	7711
5531	7808
5532	7809
5792	7930
5798	7931

```
0  5  7  9  8  6  9  9  7  4  4
1  0  6  1  7  8  8  9  0  9  3
1  0  9  8  0  1  7  9  1  5  1
6  7  5  4  7  6  2  8  6  0  5
4  1  9  5  7  0  3  0  2  6  1
2  0  9  1  6  3  1  2  7  0  1
7  6  2  2  0  9  0  9  4  6  7
9  8  8  0  7  0  8  3  3  6  1
8  6  7  6  1  9  9  1  8  1  0
4  1  1  0  3  6  7  6  3  0  1
4  0  8  8  5  1  0  5  1  6  7
```

The solution is on page 81.

HIDDEN NUMBERS

Here's another number puzzle that adds up to a rewarding search. See above for complete solving directions.

2201	4088
2209	4089
2460	4479
2461	4489
2674	5311
2686	5317
2871	5501
2878	5509
3151	5797
3171	5798
3380	5967
3381	5969

"P" MOVIES

The 26 "p" movies in the Word List have been packed into the petite puzzle presented here. Can you peruse the diagram and pluck them out with the particular panache of the premier puzzler?

PACK (The)
PAID
PALEFACE (The)
PALM BEACH STORY (The)
PANDORA'S BOX
PARDNERS
PARENTS
PARNELL
PARTY (The)
PATSY (The)
PATTON
PAULA
PAYDAY
PERFECT

PHANTASM
PICNIC
PIED PIPER (The)
PILOT (The)
PINK PANTHER (The)
PINOCCHIO
POPI
POPPY
POSSE
POWER (The)
PRIZE (The)
PSYCHO

```
W P I E D P I P E R D N G Y
P A N D O R A S B O X I P P
I R P W P R S D I G A L A O
N D E F N O I H C C O N I P
K R C E P S R E N D R A P P
P A L M B E A C H S T O R Y
A L S T N E R A P Y P U I A
N P I V N I D F D I S O Z D
T I P I L O T E E C J T E Y
H C D V P A U L A C I V A A
E N M S A T N A H P T P T P
R I O H C Y S P A T T O N E
M C R T K A R D L Y T R A P
```

The solution is on page 81.

BIBLE STUDY

The Word List for this Bible WORD SEARCH is composed of verses 3 and 4 of John 17, just as they appear in the King James Version of the Bible. Words grouped together in the Word List will be found together in the diagram.

And this is
life
eternal,
that
they
might
know
thee
the only
true
God, and
Jesus
Christ,
whom

thou
hast
sent. I
have
glorified
thee on
the earth:
I have
finished the
work
which
thou gavest me
to do.

```
T T J E M Y S T H E E O N
E H T D E H S I N I F T M
J A O H U H W M E C Y I W
E T T U Q T T D O I G H L
A T O V G R N E H H I Y A
E H S B N A J A T C W L J
T K X I D E V A H Z H N E
E Q N O R E I E C A I O S
R U G O T H C J S V O E U
N K R O W T C T X T N H S
A N D T H I S I S T M T I
L O E J G L O R I F I E D
```

The solution is on page 81.

6

Solve this puzzle by forming an unbroken chain of circled words in which the last letter of one word is the first letter of the next. The number in parentheses beside each dash tells you the length of the word you're looking for. To start you off, the first three words have been circled and entered into the Word List.

CHARGE (6)	____ (5)	____ (7)
EXPLAIN (7)	____ (6)	____ (8)
NEAT (4)	____ (5)	____ (7)
____ (6)	____ (6)	____ (6)
____ (4)	____ (5)	____ (4)
____ (4)	____ (5)	____ (4)
____ (5)	____ (5)	____ (6)

More blanks on right column:
(6) (4) (4) (8) (5) (6) (5) (6) (4) (5) (4) (5) (5) (4) (4) (5) (4) (4) (5) (6) (5) (5) (4)

```
C Z J T H S E L K A N G A R O O O
H Z O U W A R C E Q P M N R C P S
A O M M E I O O Y A C H T E A Z R
R E E D I L S Z N V O T A Q R L O
G X R E R C C T E O N N U G G E T
E X P L A I N W X T D E T Y P E D
X M J L M E R I U I D I V A S L A
M O L O A J H C L G R D G S G M F
P L H T H G I E G N A Z D Q O O F
T A I U D R Y N O A I O A M G D Y
I R L M S E I I V T N C I N O T A
O U L P B K N F E U O A N Z L U V
N R E D N O Y G R R A R D E T M O
A L Y U S P A E N A W D M M L R W
L R D E N E T S I L E S A N U A S
```

The solution is on page 81.
Word list is on page 91.

7

TIMED: "JUST WORDS"

You'll be FLOATing on air once you've found all 49 generally unrelated words hidden in the diagram below. Our expert found them in just five minutes, 50 seconds. Can you match that time?

AGLOW

ALATE

ALPINE

AWFUL

BIRCH

BISCUIT

BLADE

BLINK

BLOCK

BOBBIN

BROKE

BUDDY

BURST

CLUMP

DEMURE

DREAM

DROLL

EXCLUDE

FLOAT

FLUTE

FRUIT

GARMENT

GARNER

GLORY

GRILL

HAUNT

HONEY

LAUGH

LOVABLE

MADLY

MAPLE

MEDAL

OUGHT

PAUSE

PETAL

PLACARD

PLUSH

SPOOF

STONY

TENSE

THROW

TIDAL

TOWEL

TWEED

TWICE

VOLUME

WANED

WATCH

YONDER

```
T W I C E W B I R C H E G P
I N O T O H W U E Y L D A M
U W U L E O L A D E M U R E
R L G A R N E R N D S L M L
F A H H H E S I O E Y C E P
T D T N G Y P E Y F D X N A
W I E M U L O V A B L E T M
E T U K A T O W E L U O B W
E D X C L E F R I I A R A F
D J A O S U R R Y N O T S T
D R O L L I G D M K C P E T
D N I B B O B D E H S U L P
```

The solution is on page 81.

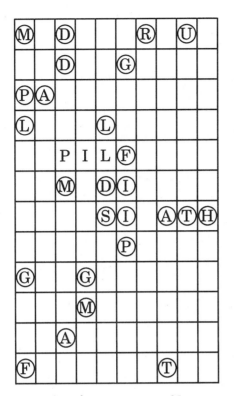

The solution is on page 81.

TANGLEWORDS

Fit the 30 words in to the blank spaces. Circled letters already entered start one or more words, and any letter may be part of more than one word. Do not go through any black squares as you fill in each word. FLIP has been entered to start you off.

ACME	ISSUE
ANAGRAM	LAMPOON
ARCHAIC	LYNX
DIAGNOSE	MEDIOCRE
DIALECT	MOPE
DIVAN	MURAL
FLAGRANT	PARLAY
FLIP	POSE
FOIST	RECEDE
GAZELLE	SOON
GEESE	SPRUCE
GOLF	TABLEAU
HANDY	THRICE
HEADSET	TRANCE
IRONY	USER

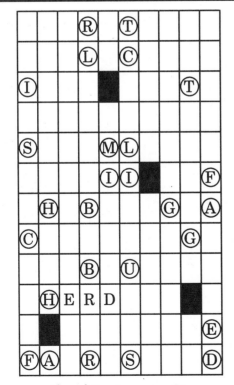

The solution is on page 81.

TANGLEWORDS

See above for solving directions; HERD has been filled in for you.

AEROSOL	IGLOO
AFFIXED	IMMUNE
BOLOGNA	LIBIDO
BOUQUET	LIMBO
CHASTISE	LUCID
COLT	MASH
DELTA	RESPOND
ENDED	ROTATED
FIASCO	ROTUNDA
FLOW	SERAPH
GLUED	SYNCOPE
GRUDGE	TACT
GUIDE	TAPIOCA
HABITAT	TORQUE
HERD	URBAN
IBEX	

NUMBER "ONE"
WORDS

Hidden in the diagram are 28 words containing the word "one." There are no foreign, slang or plural words included. We've circled STONE to help start you off.

YOUR WORD LIST

The solution is on page 82.
Word list is on page 91.

```
B Y Y D T A L E N O R D I
G E O E L E N O L O C Z S
S N N E N O L C Y C S O Y
E O Z O T O T M N A H H P
V L L N C H H R N D O O H
F A I H R X Y P R O N E O
H B I O O Z A E G E E C N
N O N E N Z T F N M L T E
E E N E E N O D N O C E L
D N P E N Y N N N N H N M
E N O T S O E E E E N O G
L E Y H T T B R S Y D T A
```

POKER HANDS

You just can't lose as you find the 26 poker hands in the diagram below. Ready to cut the deck?

A 9 3 3 3	5 5 5 5 K
A A A A 3	5 6 7 8 9
J J 10 K K	5 9 9 9 4
K 2 8 2 J	6 5 J K A
Q J 4 K A	6 6 6 10 K
Q Q Q A A	6 7 8 9 10
2 7 A A A	7 7 J J J
2 5 5 5 J	8 8 A A 4
3 3 A 7 7	8 9 10 J Q
3 4 5 6 7	8 2 2 2 2
4 4 J J J	9 9 K K K
4 4 4 J J	10 9 Q J 5
4 Q Q J J	10 J Q K A

The solution is on page 82.

```
 8  3  5  A  J  A  4  K 10  6  6  6
 8  Q  J  J  Q  Q  4  3  2  K  7  A
 A  2  J 10  9  Q  J  5  6  8  A  6
 A  K  2  A  K  Q  J  7  9  3  2  J
 4  K  5  2  A  Q  J 10  6  4  6  J
 J  Q  5  Q  2  A  6  K  9  Q  K 10
 6  J  5  5  7  A  A  9  9  8  J  K
 3  4  J  6  5  6  9  3  K  Q  J  K
 2  3  5  7  6  5  7  3  K  J  4  2
 2  4  3  8  7  J  6  A  K  4  4  6
 3  Q  J  9  6  K  4  7  Q  K  4  7
10  6  4  6  A  A  A  7  2  A  2  A
```

HIDDEN ANSWER: *JULIUS CAESAR*

What observant quotation from William Shakespeare's Julius Caesar is hidden in the diagram below? To find out, circle the 33 characters in the Word List. The UNUSED letters will spell out the hidden answer when read from left to right.

```
S  U  I  L  B  U  P  S  U  I  V  A  L  F  S  T
S  H  S  L  E  A  B  U  U  U  S  E  C  S  U  P
U  S  U  D  I  P  E  L  O  I  V  I  U  F  I  G
I  R  I  S  E  G  A  L  T  A  N  R  N  N  C  E
L  L  D  U  S  S  A  U  R  N  O  M  D  I  U  S
I  S  U  I  N  A  D  R  A  D  W  A  U  H  L  E
P  N  A  C  T  I  O  A  I  N  R  U  P  L  A  C
O  T  L  E  I  R  M  M  D  U  I  M  S  T  O  J
P  C  C  D  E  L  E  E  S  C  S  E  I  S  L  V
O  O  T  C  C  T  I  B  S  I  A  T  N  U  E  O
R  S  I  A  R  A  R  U  O  S  I  E  R  C  N  T
T  C  E  A  V  U  S  M  S  N  A  L  S  R  A  A
I  A  S  U  T  I  L  C  I  O  I  L  R  A  S  R
A  T  E  U  F  R  U  U  A  O  M  U  A  M  R  T
P  O  S  O  W  E  S  S  R  C  A  S  S  I  U  S
```

The solution and the hidden answer are on page 82.

ARTEMIDORUS
BRUTUS
CAESAR
CALPURNIA
CASCA
CASSIUS
CATO
CICERO
CINNA
CLAUDIUS
CLITUS
DARDANIUS
DECIUS
FLAVIUS
LENA
LEPIDUS
LIGARIUS
LUCILIUS
LUCIUS
MARCUS
MARULLUS
MESSALA
METELLUS
OCTAVIUS
PINDARUS
POPILIUS
PORTIA
PUBLIUS
STRATO
TITINIUS
TREBONIUS
VARRO
VOLUMNIUS

Each year, usually in the month of January, the National Football League holds its Pro Bowl, with the two conferences (NFC and AFC) competing. Outstanding players are chosen from each conference based on the season's performance. The victorious NFC squad members are listed below.

ANDERSEN (Morten)
ANDERSON (Neal)
ARNOLD (Jim)

BROWNER (Joey)

CARTER (Anthony; Michael)

CASE (Scott)
COFER (Mike)
CRAIG (Roger)
CUNNINGHAM (Randall)
DOLEMAN (Chris)
DUERSON (Dave)
ELLARD (Henry)
FRALIC (Bill)
GRAY (Jerry)
HALEY (Charles)
HILGENBERG (Jay)
JACKSON (Keith)
JORDAN (Steve)
KINARD (Terry)
LEE (Carl)
LOTT (Ronnie)
MANN (Charles)
MARTIN (Eric)
MAY (Mark)
MILLARD (Keith)
MILLS (Sam)
NEWBERRY (Tom)
SETTLE (John)
SHARPE (Luis)
SINGLETARY (Mike)
SLATER (Jackie)
SMITH (Doug; J. T.)
STUDWELL (Scott)
TAYLOR (John; Lawrence)
WALKER (Herschel)
WHITE (Reggie)
WILSON (Wade)
WOLFLEY (Ron)
ZIMMERMAN (Gary)

```
R F S Q T F V R U N O S K C A J
E X R H A L E Y D O I E R Y H W
T O Z A Y K E R C S L T V G H B
A M D O L E M A N R M T R I A C
L A S A O I S T J E K L T A H A
S Q W L R E C E W U W E A R M R
E T T O L Z M L M D C B O C H T
K C U N N I N G H A M P E R S E
I O Q D L M M N C O W L A R Y R
N F N L W M H I L G E N B E R G
A E A N D E R S E N D H L N I Y
R R L E S R L P I E N F O W L E
D W V F A M R L R M L T O O G E
D L O N R A I S A O N A D R O J
E T C O H N O T W R E N A B A B
W I L S O N O T H E D Y A M E Y
```

The solution is on page 82.

12

1989 PRO BOWL: AFC

In the annual NFL Pro Bowl, the AFC (American Football Conference) meets the NFC (National Football Conference) in the Pro Bowl. We've listed 40 members of the AFC squad for you to find in the diagram.

BENNETT (Cornelius)
BROOKS (James)
BROWN (Eddie; Tim)
CHERRY (Deron)
CHILDRESS (Ray)
CLAYTON (Mark)
CONLAN (Shane)
DICKERSON (Eric)
DIXON (Hanford)
DONALDSON (Ray)
FULCHER (David)
GRIMSLEY (John)
HILL (Drew)
HINTON (Chris)
HOLMAN (Rodney)
HORAN (Mike)
HULL (Kent)
ILKIN (Tunch)
KRIEG (Dave)
LEWIS (Albert)
MATTHEWS (Bruce; Clay)
MCMILLAN (Erik)
MILLEN (Matt)
MINNIFIELD (Frank)
MONTOYA (Max)
MOON (Warren)
MUNCHAK (Mike)
MUNOZ (Anthony)
NORWOOD (Scott)
PORTER (Rufus)
REMBERT (Johnny)
ROZIER (Mike)
SHULER (Mickey)
SMERLAS (Fred)

SMITH (Bruce)
SOCHIA (Brian)
STEPHENS (John)

TIPPETT (Andre)
TOON (Al)
WILLIAMS (Lee)

```
S Y H C N N M S M D O H N P J A
K H B R O O K S L C N W O R B N
A A U H L O S E Q E M R S R I C
H Y E L S M I R G A T I D K A O
C T U H E F I D E E H O L M A N
N H M I I R W L R K F I A L Y L
U N U N E L L I M U C Z N N A A
M O N T O Y A H L X Q I O O U N
N I O O Z T S C A L A X D L O O
M A Z N R T H M S T I P P E T T
M A T T H E W S A D H A E W A Y
K Q U E R N M R L I C O M I Z A
R M Z R E N A B R E O P Q S L L
I O Y S N E H P E T S L A L I C
E X J I C B Z A M R O Z I E R E
G N O R W O O D S E T H T I M S
```

The solution is on page 82.

13

SYMBOL SEARCH

Each of the 26 letter and symbol combinations listed begins with a letter of the alphabet. Can you do a letter-perfect job of finding them in the diagram?

A + % : $ N @ – % +
B / – & ?   O $! = &
C # = @ +   P + @ / ?
D : / ! –   Q / # $ *
E ! @ * ?   R ! % @ –
F @ & + :   S + & : /
G – * ? =   T % * ? !
H : $ # %   U # : – $
I & ! / *   V * = % #
J = + : ?   W – ? & @
K ? – $!   X ? $ * =
L $ @ # =   Y & + ! %
M % : & /   Z = / # :

```
+ A + : K F * / ! & I X !
? % T ? P + @ / ? B / ? X
U # – I & : = & K ? * $ $
O $ + @ = # C : + % / * &
! : : # N / S % T : J = W
% H Y % : = + M % V ! G –
Z ! P & + Z R V * $ # / Q
J = + : ? A ! = O & D L W
! S : & E * % U # : – $ –
D : – @ Y # @ – / @ F @ ?
Q / H : C # – ! R ! $ * &
B N @ = ? * – G E M % L @
```

The solution is on page 82.

GROANER: SOUPS

How do you make soup golden? To find out, circle the types of soups listed below. The UNUSED letters, read left to right, will reveal the amusing answer.

ALPHABET   MINESTRONE
AVOCADO   MISO
BEAN   MUSHROOM
CABBAGE   ONION
CELERY   OXTAIL
CHEESE   PEA
CHICKEN   PLUM
CLAM   POTATO
CORN   PUMPKIN
EGG DROP   TOMATO
FISH   VEGETABLE
HOT POT   WON TON

```
W O N T O N T O P T O H
A V O C A D O T A T O P
Y T E B A H P L A O O U
P Y G G P L U M U T N F
M R G I E N O X T A I L
O E D F N T O U R S O E
O L R R B E A N H T N G
R E O E E N K B C A M A
H C P O R R O C L T A B
S E S E E H C S I E L B
U I N I K P M U P H C A
M I N E S T R O N E C C
```

The solution and the hidden answer are on page 82.

D O U R S T P T A M Z Y O A
T N W O U U L M L W O B T P
W A U B P R E L A T I O N S
E Z H O E I A M M V Q L A E
N Y M T R Q S T T Y E S T S
T D F T I X E L E V E R L S
Y A R D O M A A N O U V I I
R R G E R M Q U D D U L L O
O B M I S V E Q G Q N B A N
M Z Q G R L N E R U Y A U B
U N T N D P D Q U A O L L L
H S A S P R S M B A L I M B

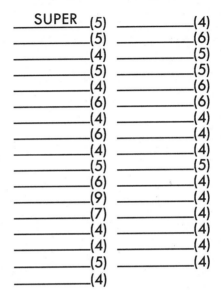

TAIL TAG

See page 5 for solving directions.

SUPER _____ (5)	_____ (4)
_____ (5)	_____ (6)
_____ (4)	_____ (5)
_____ (5)	_____ (5)
_____ (4)	_____ (6)
_____ (6)	_____ (6)
_____ (4)	_____ (4)
_____ (6)	_____ (4)
_____ (4)	_____ (4)
_____ (5)	_____ (5)
_____ (6)	_____ (4)
_____ (9)	_____ (4)
_____ (7)	_____ (4)
_____ (4)	_____ (4)
_____ (4)	_____ (4)
_____ (5)	_____ (4)
_____ (4)	

The solution is on page 82.
Word list is on page 91.

M O O S E M E E S O O M
O E S M O O S E M O M S
E S O O M O O S E O O M
S O O E M S O E O M O E
M O O S E E M S E O S S
S M M O S M E O S O E O
E S O O M E E S O O M O
S E O M O O S M O S M M
O M S O E S O O M O E S
O M E O S M E O O E M M
M O E S O O M S E M O O
S O O E O M E E S O O M

TRACK THE "MOOSE"

There are 31 MOOSE hidden somewhere in the diagram below. Get out your hunting caps, solvers, and see if you can use your tracking talents to bag them all!

The solution is on page 82.

TYPES OF LETTERS

There are 25 kinds of correspond-ence sealed into the special-delivery diagram; we know you can open it up and sort this mixed-up mail with great dispatch.

AIR
BUSINESS
CHAIN
CIRCULAR
CREDENCE
CREDIT
DEAD
DELEGATION
DIMISSORY
DROP
FAN
FORM
INTRO-
    DUCTION
LOVE
MARQUE
MONITORY
NEWS
OPEN
OVERT
PASCHAL
PASTORAL
PATENT
PERSONAL
POISON-
    PEN
REQUEST

```
Y N E W S T N E T A P W N
R S S E N I S U B R O O X
O E C N E D E R C W I M V
S P Q M O L A R O T S A P
S A T U V I M V C Q O R E
I S I W E H T U B O N Q R
M C D D R S D A Q C P U S
I H E L T O T V G O E E O
D A R M R O F L R E N W N
D L C T X Y S D H V L A A
M O N I T O R Y W O F E L
N I A H C I R C U L A R D
```

The solution is on page 83.

QUOTESEARCH: BELLOC

Many people know exactly how they would like to be remembered, and Joseph Belloc (1870–1953), British writer and historian, was no exception; his self-description is below. Words grouped together will be found together in the dia-gram.

Joseph
Belloc,
author
and
historian,
once
wrote
this
bit of
verse
about
himself:
"When
I am
dead,
I hope
it may
be said:
'His sins
were
scarlet,
but
his
books
were read.' "

```
E H I M S E L F A L I R
Y P M F E M E O B O T D
L E O C N B U T O U H A
A S N H J H C I O W I E
J O W W I O B B K R S R
D J T E L R A C S R W E
I A B L R C U Q E E V R
A T E Z O E T V F M A E
S B M D K R H S T H A W
E S N A I R O T S I H W
B A I W Y G R E F E A L
E S D H I S S I N S Z M
```

The solution is on page 83.

```
M M N D I V A D E J S
U I E M J O N A H A I
H C O R L S J V R C M
A A E Y D O R E H O O
N H D R L Y T U S B N
M I J A M E S E Q U Q
A B Y G P S S U L T S
E A C A E S O H I M M
E L I H U E A T A Q U
H A I I Q J U R I A H
A K A A U S B Q A I D
C G E Q S A D U J H E
```

The solution is on page 83.

BIBLE CHARACTERS

The 26 terms in the Word List are all five-letter names found in the Bible. From AARON to URIAH, try to find these characters in the Greatest Story Ever Told.

AARON	JESUS
ABRAM	JONAH
BALAK	JUDAS
DAVID	LYDIA
ELIAS	MICAH
ELIHU	MOSES
GAIUS	NAHUM
HAGAR	NAOMI
HEROD	PETER
HOSEA	SARAH
JACOB	SIMON
JAMES	TITUS
JESSE	URIAH

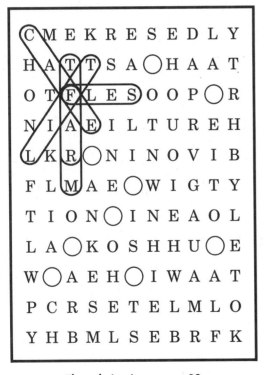

The solution is on page 83.
Word list is on page 91.

JACKPOT 1

Place a consonant within each circled blank to form the maximum number of four-letter words. We've done one for you. If you choose correctly, you will hit the Jackpot for 40 words. Your consonants are: B, C, G, L, N, P, R, S, T.

Charleston, South Carolina, is a major southeastern port; among its industries are chemicals and steel. The oldest city in the state, it is also a major tourist center, known for its beautiful houses, monuments and streets, 39 of which are hidden in the diagram below.

ASHLEY (Ave.)

ASHTON

ATLANTA

BARRE

BEAUFAIN

BLAKE

BOGARD

BROAD

CALHOUN

CANNON

CHAPEL

CHIME

COLONIAL

CONE

COOK

DELSEY

DUNCAN

FIFE

GEORGE

JUDITH

KING

LEGARE

LIBERTY

LINE

LOGAN

MARY

MEETING

MONTAGUE (Ave.)

NUNAN

QUEEN

REID

SMITH

SOCIETY

SOUTH

TRADD

TRUMBO

WARREN

WATER

WEST

```
G N I T E E M B N A G O L A
T A K H N N K O O C B Q S N
D N C I O M K G N M B H D I
I U L N N B A A U T L D R A
E N N L E G A R E E A W N F
R A E C E F T D Y R K G W U
C B R O A D E T T E E E U A
O J R L M N R M E F S V Q E
N G A O R E S M I T H L U B
E R B N B E L F C H A P E L
J U D I T H T U O S C Z E D
A T L A N T A A S H T O N Y
D C A L H O U N W A R R E N
```

The solution is on page 83.

CHILDREN'S AUTHORS

The 41 authors in the Word List below are well-known for their work in children's literature. For instance, DOCTOR SEUSS has been a favorite of many generations of children, as has his most famous character, the Cat in the Hat. See how many of these pleasing penners you can find in the diagram.

AIKEN (Joan)
ALCOTT (Louisa May)
ALEXANDER (Lloyd)
ANDERSEN (Hans Christian)
BARRIE (J.M.)
BAUM (L. Frank)
BLUME (Judy)
BOND (Michael)
CARROLL (Lewis)
CLEARY (Beverly)
DAHL (Roald)
DICKENS (Charles)
DOCTOR SEUSS
EDWARDS (Julie)
FITZHUGH (Louise)
GRIMM (The Brothers)
KIPLING (Rudyard)
KLEIN (Norma)
KONIGSBURG (E.L.)
L'ENGLE (Madeleine)
LEWIS (C.S.)
LOFTING (Hugh)
MCDONALD (George)
NORTON (Mary)
PECK (Richard)
POTTER (Beatrix)
REY (H.A.)
ROCKWELL (Thomas)
RODGERS (Mary)
SELDEN (George)
SIDNEY (Margaret)

SILVERSTEIN (Shel)
SINGER (Isaac Bashevis)
STEVENSON (Robert Louis)
TOLKIEN (J.R.R.)

TRAVERS (P.L.)
TWAIN (Mark)
VERNE (Jules)
WHITE (E.B.)
WILDER (Laura Ingalls)
WILLIAMS (Jay)

```
E L A G N O R G R U B S G I N O K L
L I O N E R V E R N E S C T R I N A
G U S I D N E Y O M O R E O P C H I
N P O T T E R O C A R R O L L C N K
E L L F I O R D K C I N I K D L C E
L L B O N D O S W E H N S I L E R N
E E K L O N O R E R G S T E P A N O
D W O S A R O N L N U R R N I R H S
W I L L I A M S L W H I T E N Y S N
A S D O R L R A N O Z H U H V U L E
R E A D E E V N O R T O N S E A L V
D B H U G H Z E R S I L M S W I R E
S A L D N K C A R T F G R I M M H T
C R O W I L D E R S T O E E L L T S
B R I N S E C K E R T O Y L M O L L
N I A W T I N D I C K E N S C U R N
V E R N O N T R O L L T I L M S L W
T A L E X A N D E R T R A N M U A B
```

The solution is on page 83.

FIND THE "PUPPY"S

There are 39 PUPPYs scampering about in the diagram. Can you find them all?

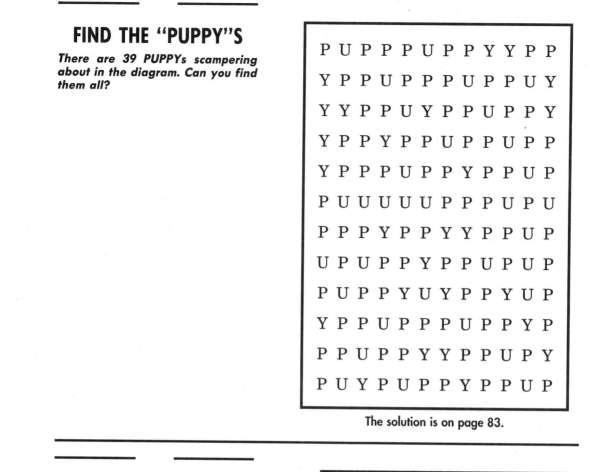

```
P U P P P U P P Y Y P P
Y P U P P P U P P U Y
Y Y P P U Y P P U P P Y
Y P P Y P P U P P U P P
Y P P U P P Y P P U P
P U U U U P P P U P U
P P P Y P P Y Y P P U P
U P U P P Y P P U P U P
P U P P Y U Y P P Y U P
Y P P U P P P U P P Y P
P P U P P Y Y P P U P Y
P U Y P U P P Y P P U P
```

The solution is on page 83.

POETRY SEARCH: LEAR

The Word List describes a "hairy" housing problem, told in verse by English humorist and artist Edward Lear (1812-88). Words grouped together will be found together.

There	a Hen,
was an	Four
Old Man	Larks
with	and a
a beard,	Wren
Who	Have
said:	all
"It is	built
just as	their
I feared!	nests
Two	in my
Owls	Beard."
and	

```
J E N D N A N A L O S
E D I E R A H E N L S
O A R R S A L R W D Y
S H M A V T E O Z M A
K Q W E E Y S B N A Q
R U O F W B Z I R N B
A M D I P S A T S U J
L H T K W N L W I L P
T H E I R T L L T Y R
L C E R E H T G I W E
Y E D F N B W E C R O
```

The solution is on page 83.

20

RECIPE: CREOLE CRAB MEAT CASSEROLE ━━━━━━

Here's a succulent seafood dish that's easy to prepare for lunch or dinner. The terms in the Word List are taken directly from the recipe below, and are hidden in the diagram. Bon appétit!

BUTTERED	FLOUR	SHERRY
CANS	GREEN	SIMMER
CATSUP	LARGE	SIZE
CHILI	LIGHT	SKILLET
CHOPPED	MELT	STIR
CLAM	PARSLEY	TABLESPOON
CRAB MEAT	PIMENTOS	TEASPOON
CREAM	REMOVE	TOAST
DASH	SALT	UNTIL
DRAINED	SAUTÉ	WORCESTERSHIRE
FLAKED		

RECIPE

1/3 cup butter or margarine
1 cup chopped onion
1 cup chopped green pepper
3 cans (6 1/2 oz. size) flaked crab
  meat
1/4 cup flour
1/2 cup catsup or chili sauce
1 tablespoon Worcestershire sauce
1 cup clam juice
1/2 teaspoon salt
dash pepper
4 oz. pimentos, drained and
  chopped
1/3 cup sherry
3 cups light cream
2 tablespoons chopped parsley
toast triangles, buttered

In a large skillet, melt butter or margarine. Sauté green pepper and onion until soft, then remove from heat. Add flour, catsup, Worcestershire sauce, cream, clam juice, salt and pepper; stir. Bring to a boil; then reduce heat and simmer for about 7-8 minutes. Add crab meat, sherry, and pimentos; stir well. Heat just until hot. Garnish with parsley. Serve with toast triangles. Makes 8 servings.

```
N O O P S A E T B M A E R C
G D C A N S O R E M M I S C
P R F C R A B M E A T D Q L
U A W N S U T U B S B M N K
S I R T H T T U T R U O L F
T N X S M E L T J T O C K L
A E I E L C H O P P E D G A
C D S L M E N Q S I D R F K
P Q I Q I A Y E J M E N E E
H K Z W O H L S H E R R Y D
S R E I Y B C C N N M G L I
A E G R A L S A L T H G I L
D U N T I L R E M O V E Z H
W O R C E S T E R S H I R E
```

The solution is on page 83.

Most of the words in the list can be found in the diagram as it is; some, however, use missing letters (shown by blocks). It's up to you to determine which letter goes in each block. The mystery letters, when read in order, will reveal a message related to the theme. Good luck!

ZABCIKVILLE (TX)	ZELMA (IN)	ZITTLESTOWN (MD)
ZACHARY (LA)	ZENAS (IN)	ZOAR (CT)
ZACHOW (WI)	ZENDA (KS)	ZOE (KY)
ZAFRA (OK)	ZENIA (CA)	ZOLFO SPRINGS (FL)
ZAG (KY)	ZENITH (IL)	ZONE (OH)
ZAHL (ND)	ZENORIA (LA)	ZOOK (KS)
ZAIDEE (GA)	ZENT (AR)	ZORA (MO)
ZALESKI (OH)	ZENZ CITY (OH)	ZORN (TX)
ZAMA (MS)	ZEONA (SD)	ZORTMAN (MT)
ZANDER (WI)	ZEPP (VA)	ZUEHL (TX)
ZANETA (IA)	ZERBE (PA)	ZULA (KY)
ZANONI (VA)	ZERKEL (MN)	ZULLINGER (PA)
ZANTE (CA)	ZERO (MS)	ZULU (IN)
ZAP (ND)	ZETELLA (GA)	ZUNI (NM)
ZAPATA (TX)	ZETTO (GA)	ZUNKERVILLE (TX)
ZARAH (KS)	ZETUS (MS)	ZUTPHEN (MI)
ZAVALLA (TX)	ZEVELY (WV)	ZWINGLE (IA)
ZEBA (MI)	ZILLAH (WA)	ZWOLLE (LA)
ZEELAND (MI)	ZIM (MN)	ZYBACH (TX)
ZELA (WV)	ZINC (AR)	ZYLKS (LA)
ZELIENOPLE (PA)	ZITTAU (WI)	ZZYZX (CA)
ZELL (MO)		

22

```
Z S A N E Z E T E L L A H Y
I O L H E U Z E E L A N D L
L Z L N K L E K Z Z A M A E
L I I [       ] O Z V
A T A Z O E L N N Z P A U E
H T R I Z S O A D A F L T Z
Z L O T I R P A A R Z L P E
W E Z T I K T R A A O A H L
I [       ] A I [     ] L
N T G U N E E M N R A N I
G O T A S D Z H L L G Z Z
L W Z R Z Q E E F A E S A K
E N Z U A H Y R B O Z Z I I
R [     ] C T [     ] C
E N R Y O K E A I E I L E B
G E T R N L E T B C Z I E A
N Z M A I Y L R A Y Z E T Z
I Z A H L Z E E V T Z N G Z
L E N C F [   ] I A O E Y
L N N A H N T R L L L P A Z
U I S Z U O O E U H P L A X
Z A L Z A Z W Z E L A E E Z
```

The solution and hidden message are on page 90.

23

Tagalog is one of the official languages of the Philippines, and is native to Manila, the country's capital. Listed below are the cardinal numbers of this language; as you try to find them in the diagram, you might want to add them to your personal language repertoire.

```
Z A U Q U O L T A T G N I B A L
J Y P U H O B I L G N A S I A A
P H L A V O L L M G D Y U B K B
O L T A T S C A Z A V A I F L I
T H U I B L Y B W Z U N L M V N
I M P H Y I X I N G G H A A H G
P H U L M Y N N J A N I B C W D
G N P I T U N G P U S I J Q U A
N A J M S C Y A L G S Z B M H L
I A Z A Z A T N N I Z O Z A Z A
B D Y N Y N Y I A Y M L Y I L W
A G H G A J B M J I X A V S P A
L N P P X A N N N G H W Q U O N
Q A U U L A L A B I N G I S A G
U S A M P U U P G N U L A W X P
E I Q U P G N U L T A T S I Q U
```

The solution is on page 84.

(1) ISA
(2) DALAWA
(3) TATLO
(4) APAT
(5) LIMA
(6) ANIM
(7) PITO
(8) WALO
(9) SIAM
(10) SAMPÛ
(11) LABING ISA
(12) LABING
   DALAWA
(13) LABING
   TATLO
(14) LABING
   APAT
(15) LABING
   LIMA
(16) LABING
   ANIM
(17) LABING
   PITO
(18) LABING
   WALO
(19) LABING
   SIAM
(20) DALAWANG
   PÛ
(30) TATLUNG
   PÛ
(40) APAT NA PÛ
(50) LIMANG PÛ
(60) ANIM NA
   PÛ
(70) PITUNG PÛ
(80) WALUNG
   PÛ
(90) SIAM NA
   PÛ
(100) ISANG
   DAAN
(1000) ISANG
   LIBO

COUNTING IN HEBREW

In this puzzle, the Word List consists of cardinal numbers in Hebrew, but don't worry—you don't have to be fluent to find them in the diagram. All you need are sharp eyes and a sharp pencil for this WORD SEARCH. Good luck!

(0) EFES
(1) ECHAD
(2) SCHNAYIM
(3) SCHLOSCHAH
(4) ARBA
(5) CHAMISCHAH
(6) SCHISCHAH
(7) SCHIVAH
(8) SCHMONAH
(9) TISCHAH
(10) ASARAH
(11) ACHAD ASSAR
(12) SCHNAYIM ASSAR
(13) SCHLOSC-HAH ASSAR
(14) ARBA ESREH
(15) CHAMISC-HAH ASSAR
(16) SCHISCHAH ASSAR
(17) SCHIVAH ASSAR
(18) SCHMONAH ASSAR
(19) TISCHAH ASSAR
(20) ESSRIM
(30) SCHLO SCHIM
(40) ARBAIM
(50) CHAMI SCHIM
(60) SCHISCHIM
(70) SCHIVIM
(80) SCHMONIM
(90) TISCHIM
(100) MEAH
(1000) ELEF

```
Z Y C H A M I S C H A H E S S R I M
R Y T X H A H C S O L H C S C S C E
Z A M I Y A N H C S Z H H H H C C L
R Q S C H I V I M M I A A X N H Y E
S A Z S M M V S X S R M Q U A I J F
C F S Z A Q I C C A I M Q D Y V R Y
H C S S C H Z H S S C C R V I A V E
I B B B A Q A A C H J A Z A M H F M
S T I S C H A H A S S A R R A E S I
C T C Z A Q A M C S O B V N S R C H
H J I S K H I V A S A L O V S S H C
I K S S A S A D I I O M H H A E M S
M A M S C Z A R M H H L O C R A O I
R E S H V H B N B C C X H Z S B N T
Z A I L C H A X S A V S Y C U R I V
R M R A S S A H A N O M H C S A M Y
```

The solution is on page 84.

The 76 paired names that make up the Word List below should be familiar to most solvers. Each pair is connected by one letter in the diagram, so that once you've found one, the other is not too far away. See how quickly you can locate them all.

ABBOTT–COSTELLO

ANTONY–CLEOPATRA

BATMAN–ROBIN

BONNIE–CLYDE

BURKE–HARE

BURNS–ALLEN

CAIN–ABEL

CAPTAIN–TENNILLE

CASTOR–POLLUX

DAGWOOD–BLONDIE

DAMON–PYTHIAS

DAVID–GOLIATH

ERNIE–BERT

GILBERT–SULLIVAN

HECKLE–JECKLE

HI–LOIS

HOLMES–WATSON

JACK–JILL

JAN–DEAN

LAUREL–HARDY

LAVERNE–SHIRLEY

LERNER–LOEWE

LEWIS–CLARK

MARTIN–LEWIS

MASON–DIXON

NIXON–AGNEW

OZZIE–HARRIET

PETER–GORDON

PUNCH–JUDY

ROCKY–BULLWINKLE

RODGERS–HAMMERSTEIN

ROMEO–JULIET

ROMULUS–REMUS

ROSENCRANTZ–GUILDENSTERN

SACCO–VANZETTI

SIMON–GARFUNKEL

TARZAN–JANE

VICTORIA–ALBERT

26

```
W A E M N A L I N R A S O L I N D E R O T D
E T E N N I L L E E R K C A J U L I E T E R
N I X O N H A M M E R S T E I N I M V O L A
G S M R A B S T G A N O S I L G O L I A T H
A A O N E R L D P L R I S L L R E D T R D K
D I D A G W O O D A O T H L P E T E R A H L
C H H L O R B S N L C S I W E L K Y E O N E
L T O R R N M C E D C C R N A R H D N C G K
Y Y L T E W E O L N I O L V U A U R O S I N
D P M U A N I S T B C E E B R N E A G T O U
E S E T L R R T I E B R Y K T O H L M O F
I I S L O L O E R W N O A R S O M D I N L R
D O N B O B A L L E E P A N N N C S N A J A
N I I N B A B L R E O L E S T Y B A A V G G
L N X A O O B O B E C D V A N Z E T T I R I
M A S O N B L O L E L O C C H D X U L L O P
L M B J N J Z C A I R O T C I V J B T L T E
D T U T E Z E R U S J T N O C J E J C U S L
H A R R I E T G O R U U N T A R Z A N S A K
L B N E L L A I T C P M D N T C I B S R C C
D I S B U L L W I N K L E Y D N H E C K L E
E T L D L L O N E R T Y I R O M U L U S E J
```

The solution is on page 90.

BIBLE STUDY

Here's another Bible WORD SEARCH; this time the quote is from II Thessalonians 2, verses 16 and 17.

Now our
Lord
Jesus
Christ
himself,
and God,
even
our Father,
which
hath
loved
us, and
hath given
us everlasting

consolation
and good
hope
through
grace,
Comfort
your
hearts,
and stablish
you in
every
good
word
and work.

```
O Q N C H E V T H R O U G H
A U S E V E R L A S T I N G
J I R E V O A D O U H U O H
G A R F F E H R E V Q A I A
R Y N M A J C O T K E M T T
A D O D E T I W R S S D A H
C C O S G I H O P E Y D L G
E H U G I O W E L I N Q O I
L S R R D D O F R A U O S V
Y O U I N N Q D S Q D A N E
C O R A S U A U R U O W O N
Y A N D S T A B L I S H C I
```

The solution is on page 84.

GROANER: THINGS TO WEAR

What did the tie say to the hat? To find out, circle the 26 items listed. The UNUSED letters will spell out the rib-tickling reply when read from left to right.

BANDANNA
BELT
BERET
BLAZER
BLOUSE
BOLERO
CAPE
DRESS
FEDORA
JACKET
JEANS
JERSEY
JUMPER
KILT
KIMONO
PONCHO
ROBE
SHELL
SLACKS
SMOCK
SUIT
SWEATER
T-SHIRT
TUXEDO
UNIFORM
VEST

```
S U I T U X E D O Y S O
L M B U G O F O Y H W N
A A O D R E S S E H E C
C V L C D E A L S D A T
K I E O K J L B R P T R
S L R S E B O R E L E I
E A O A T R O H J R R H
S A N N E G A N R E E S
U S O Z O H C N O P T T
O B A N D A N N A M L U
L L N M R O F I N U I D
B E L T T E K C A J K K
```

The solution and the hidden answer are on page 84.

28

```
T N M P I W K L O H
D N E S P Y I ○ M Y
E R S H T ○ B N E L
T Y H E T L E D T P
O K N ○ Y C S T ○ R
W J E L R E H N M W
I B V T L D T ○ L L
S T ○ P A L R M P F
R L T N ○ P L E L O
L B E R D O N ○ E B
Y H K S E M W T F M
```

JACKPOT

This time, place the correct vowels in the circled blanks to form the maximum number of four-letter words (we've done the first ones for you). See if you can hit the Jackpot for 39 words. Good luck!

The solution is on page 84.
Word list is on page 91.

```
S A G A L A D K E H
W R E D T S ○ R F N
C R ○ O B A C T ○ R
A O E C E S K N O P
H T ○ B K ○ E W C E
R V B L E M D H S J
E M O L H W F ○ S T
I ○ T C ○ S V T M U
D R L R L F ○ E L E
N K G F D B T M K O
```

JACKPOT

This time the Jackpot is 37 words; can you fill in the correct vowels to obtain the greatest number of four-letter words?

The solution is on page 84.
Word list is on page 91.

The old adage that you can't tell a book by its cover is illustrated by the amusing anecdote in the Word List below. In it, we learn something new about Dr. Joyce Brothers, the well-known psychologist. Words grouped together in the Word List will be found together in the diagram.

```
W K Y G O L O H C Y S P F O K Z W K
S E S S I O N W D X S G N I X O B Q
K J S K T O X N Z H Z T W A G X U I
W F X R H H A D E R E W S N A E H S
J K I T E S O P X L K I I G S R K A
R X O E U H R U E Q X M N T A X P R
U B X O L O T V S W M I I L K S O E
O J H P V D I O E A K O L Z Y N H G
F T J E O S K E R R N O K C T O U U
Y S D W I P K C O B D D H H R I N L
T E A O J Q U W K X E O E E X T D A
X U N S R A L L O D L C T A Z S R R
I G D Z E Q Z X A O W F Y T T E E S
S L W N X P R O G R A M S O X U D I
R U O F Y T R I H T Z X B T J Q A Q
W F N Z Q X S N W O R E H A Z R N Z
O S Z X J T W I N H E R K L W J D Q
A S A D N A N O T R E P X E N A H W
```

The solution is on page 84.

Psychologist Dr. Joyce Brothers is a regular on television, both on her own programs and as a popular guest, working in her field of psychology. After a six-week cramming session, she answered questions on "The Sixty-Four-Thousand-Dollar Question," and won a total of one hundred and thirty-four thousand dollars. She proved to be an expert on boxing!

IF-FY WORDS

What witticism about "if" is hidden in the diagram below? To find out, circle the 38 listed words containing "if." After you're done, the unused letters will spell out the hidden answer.

ARTIFACT
BIFOCAL
CLASSIFY

CLIFF
DEIFY
DIFFERENCE

EDIFICE
EDIFY
ELECTRIFY
FALSIFY
FIFER
FIFTH
FIFTY
FORTIFY
JIFFY
KNIFE
MAGNIFY
MASTIFF
MODIFY
MYSTIFY
NIDIFY
NIFTY
PACIFY
RATIFY
RIFFLE
SCIENTIFIC
SHERIFF
SIMPLIFY
SKIFF
SPECIFIC
STIFF
SWIFT
TARIFF
THRIFT
TIFFANY
TRIFLE
TYPIFY
UNIFY

```
F F I K S I T H R I F T P Y
F I S N R I F F L E T T A F
Y E C I F I C E P S F F C I
F H L F E Y E F B F I I I L
I G A E G F C E F F W F P
P N S L C I N Y F I T S Y M
Y S S F L T E T T R R L I I
T T I I I A R N T A L E E S
F M F R F R E I I T W O H T
R A Y T F I F D F F I N C S
S S L A C O F I B Y T A F T
H T E S R J I D F F F Y I Y
I I I T I E D I F I C E F F
C F I F T F D I T D O I T I
N F F A F I Y R R E E Y H N
Y Y F I N G A M O D I F Y U
```

The solution is on page 90.

DOGGONE IT!

There are several systems for classifying dog breeds, most of which date back to early Roman times. In the US, the American Kennel Club groups dogs in six classes: sporting, HOUND, TERRIER, working, toy, and non-sporting. There are 116 dog breeds recognized by the American Kennel Club; 29 of them are listed here.

AFGHAN

AIREDALE

BEAGLE

BOXER

BULLDOG

CHIHUAHUA

CHOW CHOW

COLLIE

CORGI

DACHSHUND

DALMATIAN

GERMAN

   SHEPHERD

GREYHOUND

HOUND

LHASA APSO

MALTESE

MASTIFF

PEKINGESE

POODLE

PUG

PULI

RETRIEVER

SALUKI

SAMOYED

SETTER

SPANIEL

ST. BERNARD

TERRIER

VIZSLA

```
E L D O O P A L E I N A P S
I S R A R E V E I R T E R E
L G E A L S Z I V E K D O T
L R H T P M K D L I N N L T
O O P A L U A A N S A U H E
C C E E L A D T T U D H A R
H S H A K E M B I N O S S E
O A S I R I E A U A I H A I
W M N I H R N O S L N C A R
C O A I N U H G U T L A P R
H Y M A G Y A P E T I D S E
O E R T E R R H U S I F O T
W D E R E X O B U G E F F G
E L G A E B A C N A H G F A
```

The solution is on page 84.

32

NATURE'S PALETTE

"In the vaunted works of Art," wrote Ralph Waldo Emerson, "the master strokes is Nature's part." Find out what colors Nature uses to paint its fine strokes by circling the tones and tints here.

ACORN
APPLE
CANARY
CARDINAL

CHESTNUT
COCONUT
COPPER
CROCUS

EGGSHELL
FLAX
GRAPE
IRON
IVORY
JADE
LEMON
LILAC
LOBSTER
MELON
OLIVE
ORANGE
ORCHID
ORIOLE
PANSY
PEACH
PEARL
PLUM
POPPY
PUMPKIN
RAISIN
RAVEN
ROAN
ROSE
RUBY
SALMON
SAND
SOOT
STRAW
TOPAZ
VIOLET
YOLK

```
C A L I L O B S T E R O A N
O L L E H S G G E W Q V S O
C Y M O R C H I D Q A A W M
O O W T O P A Z A V N R E L
N L P E A R L E J D R L T A
U K I L W E L P P A O C X S
T Q F V U R A V E N C A C O
U C L B E M X J N L A R E O
N W A M V P V I Q G O D S T
T I X N O E K J R C W I O E
S V S P A P M A U O J N R L
E Q P I M R P S E G N A R O
H Y W U A E Y S N A P L Q I
C O P P E R U B Y R O V I V
```

The solution is on page 84.

LOOMING LARGE

In colonial times, many households had a loom, as well as a spinning wheel for making animal or plant fibers into thread. Although 18th-century spinning and weaving inventions led to today's mass-produced textiles, some of the finest silks, velvets and linens are still woven by hand. Terms associated with this art are here.

BATTEN

BOBBIN

CARD

COMB

DISTAFF

DYE

FIBER

FLAX

FLYER

HARNESS

HEDDLE

LOOM

QUILL

REED

ROVING

SHED

SHUTTLE

SPIN

SPINDLE

SPOOL

TEASEL

TREADLE

WARP

WEAVE

WEFT

WHEEL

WOOF

WOOL

WORSTED

```
S A P H E S E F O S C E T W
I H Q U I L L F H L D J I E
C A U G G D D E O R E Y L F
O H R T Y R D N A E M E D T
M S E E T B E C I E S H H L
B A B I Y L H P R A W K A W
S P I N D L E W E L O B I E
A S F A O D E T S R O W N A
N R E P D I V M L B W D H V
E R B N W S U C B O O U X E
T S E O R T N I P S O A G W
T C O E T A N U L E L P M U
A F K B D F H N R F T W S F
B M O O L F O G N I V O R O
```

The solution is on page 85.

```
8 8 5 4 0 6 1 5 9 8 1
6 4 9 7 1 7 7 9 9 7 3
4 7 6 8 9 8 9 8 4 7 8
2 5 7 5 2 4 8 7 7 6 3
7 6 7 6 4 0 9 4 8 8 5
1 8 4 5 0 2 1 1 8 6 7
8 3 6 4 5 6 7 9 9 5 4
8 1 5 0 4 4 3 4 8 9 6
9 6 6 4 2 8 7 7 5 6 4
4 7 4 5 7 8 9 1 8 4 0
3 9 8 4 6 8 8 7 8 2 0
```

The solution is on page 85.

See page 3 for solving directions.

HIDDEN NUMBERS

0045	1678
0046	1679
0192	2466
0198	2468
0287	2644
0288	2648
1354	2875
1383	2898
1477	3795
1478	3798
1594	3984
1598	3988

```
8 0 5 8 4 9 8 7 8 0 5
6 6 9 5 0 8 8 8 0 6 6
1 2 5 7 7 6 9 9 8 5 1
1 5 8 6 5 4 7 8 9 3 1
6 4 3 7 0 7 6 3 9 5 7
7 8 0 4 7 1 5 0 6 6 7
8 9 6 0 7 8 4 0 0 8 8
6 0 0 6 6 7 7 0 7 9 5
0 6 9 5 0 6 9 5 4 6 0
4 5 2 5 5 1 2 0 5 2 5
2 9 6 2 2 6 1 3 4 7 6
```

The solution is on page 85.

HIDDEN NUMBERS

1065	3476
1066	3477
1165	3565
1168	3568
1297	3670
1298	3678
1390	4705
1398	4706
2266	4890
2269	4898
2404	4987
2406	4988

TEXTILE TERRITORY

Textiles are made from various fibers by weaving, knitting, knotting, braiding, quilting and embroidering. They can be dyed, printed and sprayed in many ways. Even if your only experience with textiles is wearing them, you can sew a fine seam on this puzzle by circling the 39 types below.

BAIZE	TULLE	VELVET
BROCADE	TWEED	VOILE
BURLAP	TWILL	WOOL
CAMBRIC		
CANVAS		
CHALLIS		
CHINTZ		
COTTON		
CREPE		
DAMASK		
DENIM		
DIMITY		
DUCK		
FELT		
GAUZE		
JERSEY		
LINEN		
MADRAS		
MUSLIN		
NET		
NYLON		
PIQUÉ		
PLUSH		
POPLIN		
RAYON		
REP		
SATIN		
SEERSUCKER		
SERGE		
SILK		
SURAH		
SWISS		
TERRY		

```
C H A L L I S L I E G R E S
N L O O W A S D E E W T O S
D O N Y R R E T P B H R P I
E A T D Y A Z L E R A E Y W
N P A T E B U E R O R K E S
I M K L O S A M C C U C S I
M E L W H C G I G A S U R L
A U N I L P O P Z D V S E K
T Q S H A C N T L E F R J E
C I C L V H P O L I N E N K
I P R O I I S V L E G E D C
R U T E Q N E S T Y I S A U
B T W U R T R A Y O N N M D
M A I S B Z O T O T V R A E
A U L Y T I M I D A D E S S
C E L I O V C N S H Z C K E
```

The solution is on page 85.

POET'S CORNER

American poet Henry Wadsworth Longfellow created a body of romantic American legends in such long narratives as "The Song of Hiawatha" and "Paul Revere's Ride." Among his best-known shorter poems were the "Village Blacksmith," "Excelsior" and "The Day is Done." This final poem appears in part below.

The day
is done,
and the
darkness
Falls
from the
wings of
Night,
As a feather
is wafted
downward
From an
eagle
in his
flight.
I see
the lights
of the
village
Gleam
through
the rain
and the
mist,
And a
feeling
of sadness

comes
o'er me
That

my soul
cannot
resist.

```
Z A V L M Y S O U L D I O N
O G N I X A D A R K N E S S
J U S D V D U A D N A J T T
E T T E T E I T S E M S H D
F R O M T H E S Y L O E G R
Z E N R Y T E Q W G R M I A
W H N E J N S L L A F O L W
I T A O D V C R I E F C F N
N A C A Z E I N E G J T C W
G E S X N N O L M S H J E O
S F Q O H F I V L A I T C D
O A D I T N B G T A E S S Y
F S S H G U O R H T G L T H
I A E E S I A N D T H E G N
```

The solution is on page 85.

HAPPY LANDING

The King Khalid International Airport, in Saudi Arabia, is the largest airport in the world. It cost $3.6 billion, covers 87 square miles and has the world's highest control tower.

AGENT

BAGS

BAR

BUS

CARS

CUSTOMS

DELAY

DOMESTIC

DUTY-FREE (Shop)

FIRST CLASS

FOREIGNER

FREIGHT

GATE

IMMIGRATION

INTERNATIONAL

LANDING

LOUNGE

PASSENGER

PASSPORT

PLANE

RESERVATION

RESIDENT

RUNWAY

SIGN

SKYCAP

TAGS

TAIL

TAKEOFF

TAXI

TICKET

TOWER

WING

```
R E N G I E R O F E Z N T I
T P A S S E N G E R O A N P
W I N G M X H R A F X T E A
N F G A C O F B T I E I D S
O F I B I Y T H E R G C I S
I O S W T A G S N S N K S P
T E B U S I I A U T U E E O
A K D L E D T Z L C O T R R
R A U R M I E Y P L L A S T
G T F O O R U N W A Y G R O
I A N N D E L A Y S C N A W
M I A E P L A N E S Q Y C E
M L E R G N I D N A L V K R
I N O I T A V R E S E R X S
```

The solution is on page 85.

38

SCOTTISH ISLES

The islands surrounding Scotland are grouped into three categories. The low, irregular isles northeast of the Scottish coast are known as the Orkneys. The Shetlands (origin of the sheepdog and Shetland pony) are 50 miles north. West are the Hebrides. Chart the Scottish isles below, hidden in all directions.

ARRAN	SKYE	ULVA
BARRA	SOAY	UNST
BURRAY	ST. KILDA	WIAY
BUTE	TIREE	YELL
CANNA		
COLL		
EDAY		
EIGG		
FETLAR		
FOULA		
GIGHA		
HANDA		
HOY		
IONA		
ISLAY		
JURA		
LEWIS		
LUING		
MUCK		
MULL		
RAASAY		
RHUM		
RONA		
ROUSAY		
SANDAY		
SCARBA		

```
A R R A N Q B J N R Y A O S
R D A O Z J N S G K O C N E
R F L X U J S W S N G N I J
E V T I S S I W E L I G A U
Y T E C K A A E X G G U L N
A N F A Y T R Y M N H V L S
L B N K E I S A D N A H E T
S O R Y T A J R R F H D Y A
I H C A N N A R O R A R U J
L M R D C A N U M M A H M R
J L A E O S L B U T E B O I
Z Y U V L A W C H V T I S Y
S N U M L W K Y R A A S A Y
```

The solution is on page 85.

HORSE POWER

Lippizaners, a breed of high-spirited, WHITE horses, are trained to perform the difficult movements of *HAUTE ECOLE*, a technique in which the horse responds to barely perceptible movements of the rider. The PIROUETTE (turn in a CIRCLE) and the MEZAIR (elevated forelegs) are among the listed terms associated with Lippizaners and their centuries-old training.

BALANCE
BALLOTADE
CANTER

CAPRIOLE
CIRCLE
COURBETTE

CROUPADE
GALLOP
GRACE
HALF-PASS
HALT
HAUTE ECOLE
LEG SIGNAL
LEVADE
LUNGING
MEZAIR
PACE
PASSADE
PASSAGE
PIAFFE
PIAFFER
PIROUETTE
REINS
ROUTINE
SADDLE
SKILL
SNAFFLE
STALLION
TROT
TURNS
VIENNA
VOLTE
WALK
WHITE

```
E L A N G I S G E L C R I C
D D P R Z Q N G T T L M A O
A E A V R I A S V U I P R U
V C C S G S N I E R R H B R
E N E N S T A L L I O N W B
L A U A E A D E O L U Z S E
O L P L D D P L C V T K R T
C A C M A R E F F A I P V T
E B W S T V I F L L N I H E
E L T K O G R A L A E T F U
T P O L L A G N Z N H F E O
U O T V L A C S N E A R V R
A E R N A Z W A B I M H K I
H A L T B E D A P U O R C P
```

The solution is on page 85.

40

HARNESS UP!

Harness making is an ancient craft dating from the domestication of the horse. In one type of harness, a padded leather **COLLAR** fits over the horse's shoulder; attached **HAMES** (linked metal parts) hold the **TRACES**, or pulling straps. In another type, a neck **YOKE** holds a vehicle pole joined to the horse's **COLLAR** by a strap.

BACKSTRAP
BILLET
BIT
BLINDS
BLINKERS
BREECHING
BRIDLE
BROWBAND
CHAPE
CHINBAND
CINCH
COLLAR
CROWNBAND
CRUPPER
CURB
FACEBAND
GAG SWIVEL
GIRTH
HAMES
HAME TUG
HEALD
HIP STRAP
HITCH
KNOT
MARTINGALE
NOSEBAND

REINS
SADDLE
TERRET

TRACES
WINKER BRACE
YOKE

```
H C B A L T E P A H C A S D
C O I C O L L A R T B I R L
U N L O R E P P U R C N E A
R D L C L O A E O I Y O K E
B N E R I R W W L G O S N H
R A T C T N B N U D B E I G
E B O S A A C T B P D B L A
E N P D N R E H B A R A B G
C I S D N M B L C R N N S S
H H N E A A I R I T I D L W
I C I H C N B N E S I D R I
N S E R D A N E T K E H L V
G U R S T O R B C C N M P E
L E L A G N I T R A M I A L
T E R R E T O N K B F T W H
```

The solution is on page 85.

WHO'S GOT THE BUTTON?

Pictures have been used on garment buttons (especially metal ones) since the 1850s. Certain subjects, such as the popular CUPID on men's 19th-century coat buttons, were preferred for specific types of clothing. Forty designs that have adorned these fascinating fasteners appear here.

AIRPLANE
ANCHOR
ANIMAL
AUTOMOBILE

BALLOON
BASKET
BICYCLE
BOAT

BRIDGE
BUILDING
CASTLE
CLOWN
COIN
COMET
CRESCENT
CROSS
CUPID
ENGINE
FAN
FEATHER
FLOWER
FRUIT
GATE
GNOME
HORSESHOE
LEAF
MASK
MOON
NAIL
NUT
PIN
SHELL
SHIP
SHOES
STAR
TOWER
TRAIN
TROLLEY
UMBRELLA
WAGON

```
B U I L D I N G N O M E F J
A R E W O T A Y E L L O R T
U O C R A T S C L O W N U T
T H R Z E V C S U Q V M I C
O C E K Q W T H O P B P T E
M N S B V R O E Q R I Q J O
O A C C A S T L E N C D F H
B I E I O L Q L F O Y F E S
I L N F Z I L N T O C A A E
L C T Q A A N O A M L N T S
E Z C O M E T G O P E Q H R
E G D I R B L A B N I O E O
J E N I G N E W J Q E H R H
I A I R P L A N E S M A S K
```

The solution is on page 86.

THIMBLE TALK

Originally designed to protect the finger while sewing, thimbles are prized by collectors, who pay astonishing amounts for the most beautiful kinds. These small, bell-shaped gadgets, made chiefly of plastic or soft metal, have also been produced in the other materials mentioned below.

AGATE

AMBER

BAS-RELIEF

BISQUE

BRASS

BRONZE

CHINA

CLOISONNE

COPPER

DELFT

ENAMEL

FILIGREE

GLASS

GOLD

IVORY

LEAD CRYSTAL

MILLEFIORE

MIRROR

MOSAIC

ONYX

OXIDE

PAPIER-MACHE

PETIT POINT

PEWTER

PINE

PORCELAIN

POTTERY

SILVER

STONE

WOOD

```
G I C L C L O I S O N N E P
E M I R R O R V A E I L A O
N I A L E C R O P N T E S C
O Q S W I P O R A A M A S S
T R O X I D E Y P M I D G O
S O M N G O R I I E M C E A
D R E I A O M L E L O R N E
R E B M A N L A R I S Y Y E
G V X I R E I D M S D S O R
R L I Y F Z O H A S E T C G
E I A I N N O R C E L A O I
T S O S I O B A H L F L P L
W R S E S R Y R E T T O P I
E U Q S I B A S R E L I E F
P E T I T P O I N T M A R I
```

The solution is on page 86.

IN GOD WE TRUST

In God We Trust is a phrase that many of us are familiar with, but how many of us know its origin? The passage below gives an historical account of the famous phrase, which was designated as the US National Motto in 1956.

The US
National
Motto
was born
during the
Civil War
when
Union
morale
was low.
A clergyman
wrote to
Treasury
Secretary
Salmon
Chase,
suggesting
"recognition
of the
Almighty God
in some
form
on our
coins."

Chase
had designs
made
with the
slogan
"In God
We Trust"
and backed
laws for
its use.
It first
appeared
on some
coins
in eighteen
sixty-four.
Ninety-one
years
later,
Congress
ordered it
inscribed
on all
U.S. currency.

```
N I N E T Y O N E H T G N I R U D
E O U S W O L S A W A S B O R N M
E S I T S U S E Y E A R S U U O S
T U A T U S C U S L A N O I T A N
H E O H I U O S M R O F U T S O U
G H N U C N N I U S Y S O N M O S
I T S S U G G E S T I N G L N T N
E E O U S H R O X T N I A O W S A
N H M T T W E I C U S S U H U U M
I T E Y E I S U S E C R E T A R Y
O F G U I T S S D C R N I A U T G
R O S D N H O D C O I N S F N E R
D E A E G T A R U S B V S O T W E
E M L R O H U S W L E M I N S I L
R O L A D E K C A B D N A L I U C
E S A E R U S T A U U S O D W O A
D N N P A O E S A H C G U S E A C
I I O P U R M S A L A W S F O R R
T R E A S U R Y C N E R R U C S U
```

The solution is on page 86.

ANIMAL CITIES

HEREFORD is the name of a breed of cattle and a city in Maryland; CURLEW is both a large wading bird and an urban area in Washington. Thirty other animal names that are also US cities and towns appear below.

ANTELOPE (MT)

BADGER (IA)

BEAR (DE)

BEAVER (PA)

BIGHORN (MT)

BUFFALO (NY)

CANARY (OR)

CHICKEN (AL)

COLT (AR)

COUGAR (WA)

COYOTE (NM)

CRANE (IN)

CROW (OR)

CURLEW (WA)

DUCK (WV)

EAGLE (NE)

ELK (WY)

FOX (OK)

GIBBON (OR)

HEREFORD (MD)

HERON (MT)

MOOSE (WY)

MUSTANG (OK)

PANTHER (WV)

PELICAN (AK)

PONY (MT)

PORCUPINE (SD)

RAVEN (VA)

SQUIRREL (ID)

TIGER (WA)

TURKEY (NC)

WOLF (WY)

```
A R I T N W L E R R I U Q S
O P E L I C A N H J E L K B
K K C H E G Y N O P V G T P
C Y L S T L B R Q O X L I D
U N O R P N E V A R O E J T
D O C O U G A R F C F S G U
M R F L D S V P M U T B E R
U E O A N T E L O P E I H K
S H B F W O R C Y I U G N E
T I D F E Z V E R N W H T Y
A R W U H R A R A E B O C J
N O B B I G E K N C Y R L X
G C U R L E W H A O D N B F
A Z N E K C I H C R A N E M
```

The solution is on page 86.

PEOPLE LAKES

For most people, the name VERONICA Lake recalls a glamourous movie star of the 1940s, but it is also a body of water in Ontario. Each of the 38 male and female names is the name of a lake located in that province.

AVA
BARBARA
DONALD
DOROTHY
DWIGHT
EDGAR
ELEANOR
EMMA
EZRA
FRANCOIS
GINA
GORDON
ISAAC
ISABEL
JANE
JASON
JILL
KEITH
LAURI
LUCAS
LUELLA
MARY
MARY JANE
MEL
MEREDITH
NADINE
NORMAN
OLGA
PAUL
RALPH

RENEE
RODERICK
RUSSELL
RYAN

SHANA
STELLA
VAUGHAN
VERONICA

```
K C I R E D O R O T H Y I B
A E N C E F R A N C O I S A
B G I E J P G Y O L N J K R
Q S N T A Y B R D P V A H B
V E A U H P L A R O N I Y A
R Z L C J T L M O I N S M R
A L L E U L I A G L O A Z A
C F E Z E L J D C F R B L G
I E T S H A N A E Y F E L D
N S S H S U Q O J R I L I E
O U A O G R K A R Z E W M Z
R F N A D I N E J M Q M I E
E H V A C E W R O N A E L E
V A U G H A N D H O E N A J
```

The solution is on page 86.

RIDDLESEARCH

Hey diddle, diddle, it's time for a riddle. A riddle comprises the word list below. Can you figure out the answer before you finish circling? Hint: Two words make up the solution.

Within   gallant   safe

my first   crew   may

yon   An anchor   find;

                                 My next,

                                 ye fair,

                                 indeed,

                                 'tis true,

                                 Without

                                 an end

                                 may

                                 bind.

                                 Without

                                 my whole

                                 we're

                                 surely

                                 lost,

                                 'Midst

                                 wintry

                                 blasts

                                 and

                                 biting

                                 frost.

```
A N E N D W M I D S T F W
T N A L L A G W X A W I D
X W A Z Y H E S Z V N N E
L T M N Q R T N J T F D E
O V I H C S I U R U R L D
S Z J S A H E Y O O O Y N
T R J L T R O Y Q H S G I
X I B I E R Q R W T T N V
E A W W F M U Y X I Z I Q
N F Y N A M M E X W Y T W
Y E O Y S U R E L Y J I Z
M Y F I R S T X D N I B X
```

The solution is on page 86.

RIDDLESEARCH

Don't take your thinking caps off yet, solvers, because we have another mind-boggling riddle for you. You'll definitely get the "point" of this puzzle once you figure out the solution.

When
Grandpa
wished
my first
to make,
My second
he would
always
take,
And
handle
it with
skill.
Now,
with
your
first
tell me
the
name,
For
whole and
second

are the
same,
So guess

it if
you
will.

```
D W I S H E D N O C E S Y M
N H H F E L D N A H Z Z C Y
O O T E L L M E T T W D O F
C L Z S N R A K H I E U J I
E E M A S P N R W W R K Q R
S A B Q D Y H M E I F Z A S
S N H N S J A C T T J L X T
E D A F B K V W G O H D L S
U R Y M I T I J L M N E L R
G M O H E T L L M A J O I I
O Z U F H W I X L K M D W F
S G L Y D L U O W E H K B H
```

The solution is on page 86.

ON THE GREEN

It is believed that golf originated when Scottish shepherds used their crooks to hit stones into rabbit holes. The sport was officially established by the Scottish Parliament in 1457. For a chance to participate in this game for all ages, circle the golf terms below and remember to shout "FORE!" for each entry you find.

ACE
APRON
BAG
BIRDIE

BOGEY
CAP
CARTS
CHIP

COURSE
CUP
DIVOT
DRIVE
FAIRWAY
FORE
FOURSOME
GLOVE
GOLF BALLS
GOLF SHOES
GREEN
GRIP
HANDICAP
HOLE IN ONE
HOOK
IRON
LINKS
LOFT
PAR
PIN
PITCH
PRO SHOP
PUTTER
SAND TRAP
SCLAFF
SCORE
SHOT
SLICE
SWING
TEES
TOUR
TWOSOME
WEDGE
WOOD

```
C A R T S C O R E T T U P S
H D R I V E M O S O W T A E
G O L F B A L L S V P A C O
S C L A F F I E C I L S I H
B O G E Y A S G U D O W D S
R M A S I R C R P T F I N F
A G H F U N I E E L T Y A L
P L O O R N O E I E F A H O
I O C U O I S N G D O W T G
T V H R I K K D E T R R N I
C E P S I S E P R O E I R R
H A D O O W I D O H W A B O
I N N M Y R U O T S I F R N
P I N E G U P A R T D N A S
```

The solution is on page 86.

ON THE ICE

A game called kalv, played on ice in the Netherlands in the early 1500s, later evolved into the action-packed sport we know as hockey. Today's professional players must have SPEED, power and BALANCE and, of course, be familiar with the hockey terms here.

ARENA
BALANCE
BASH
BLADES
BOUT
BREAKAWAY
BULLY
BUMP
CAGE
CAPTAIN
CROSSOVER
FACEOFF
FLIP SHOT
FUMBLE
GLOVES
GOALIE
GOALS
GRASP
HELMET
HOCKEY
   STICKS
ICE
KNOB
NET
PUCK
RECEIVER
RINK
ROUT
SCOOP
SCORE
SHAFT
SHIN PADS
SIX (ice)
SKATES

SLAP SHOT
SLOT
SPEED

STANLEY (Cup)
STOCKINGS
STROKE

SWAY
TEAMS
THREAD A PASS

```
P E L B M U F L I P S H O T
S S A P A D A E R H T U O R
A S K R E V I E C E R H S D
R T K C U P X I S E S B E Y
G O A L I E E D V P U E V E
S C O O P T A O A L P F O L
Y K B U M P S L L S A I L N
A I A X N S S Y A C S C G A
W N S I O E H H E L M E T T
A G H R D Y A O S K A T E S
K S C A A K F T T R C U G T
A U L W E F T E E K N O B R
E B S O I G F N A M A B H O
R N I A T P A C M L R I N K
B A L A N C E C S C O R E E
```

The solution is on page 86.

POTTERY MAKING

Pottery has played an important role in human cultural development. Egyptian paintings show a potter at his **WHEEL** as early as 3500 B.C., and the Chinese introduced **PORCELAIN** for the first time in 200 B.C.

ARGIL   CERAMICS   DECORATION
BOWL   CLAY   DELFT
BUBBLE   CONE   DESIGN
                                EARTHENWARE
                                ENAMEL
                                FIRE
                                FLYWHEEL
                                GLAZE
                                KAOLIN
                                KILN
                                OXIDIZE
                                PORCELAIN
                                POTS
                                POTTER
                                POTTERY
                                RIM
                                SALT GLAZE
                                SCULPT
                                SHARD
                                SIEVE
                                SLING
                                SLIP
                                SPIN
                                THROW
                                TILE
                                TRIM
                                VITREOUS
                                WHEEL

```
E C E R E T O G I K E N O K C
L T O D E S I G N L Z P A R E
B F B N I R E A C I A O T S R
U L A V E Z A L G T L A S C A
B E R I I S A W M I G S I U M
D D G D B Y T R N L I K X L I
E O I R O N I A L E C R O P C
C X L U W T L D V M H P O T S
O I Y E L C R E P A F T L E D
R S U O E R T I V N T H R O W
A E W H E H L Z M E G L Y A C
T E T S H S W E R I F I R Z E
I Z P T W V H Y O D R A H S S
O I Y N O C E E L B B U B E F
N D U L T P D E V F T P L U C
```

The solution is on page 87.

COAL MINING

Country singer Loretta Lynn should be familiar with many of the terms below. She remembers her father donning his HARD HAT and trekking off to the COAL MINE in order to support his family. The lode you can quarry from this Word Search are terms associated with the trade.

ANTHRACITE
BEAM
BED
BITUMINOUS
BLAST
BLOWER
COAL
DEPOSIT
DRILL
DUST
DYNAMITE
ELEVATOR
FAN
HARD HAT
LAMP
LIGHT
MINE
MINER
ORE
PICK
ROCK
SEAM
SHAFT
SHIFT
SHORING
SHOVEL
STRIP
SURFACE
TRACK

TRAIN
TRUCK
TUNNEL

UNDERGROUND
UNION
VEIN

```
D F E S E A M I G H D E V L N
G R O U L T H I Y Y U L V O V
O L I G H T R N N I V E I N G
V E B L A S T A T E N N Z X T
S V A L L P M F I U U N G H A
K O L N S I I Q U N Z U C C H
C H A H T H N C D D U T S U D
U S A E S H E E K E E Z Z I R
R F H K C A R T H P I R T S A
T B C O L G H A Q O B N U U H
Z O L K R A Q X C S X P G R B
R S U O N I M U T I B R M F D
A D U W W A N B L T T F D A Z
K N E K E E V G N I O E U C L
D R L B H G R O T A V E L E Z
```

The solution is on page 87.

PALATIAL PUZZLE

France's palace of **VERSAILLES** is a beautiful, ornate structure containing over 100 rooms. It was built by Louis XIV in the 1600s and is now a national museum housing fine paintings and sculpture. This list contains palaces throughout Europe, most of which are also museums now.

ALCAZAR (Spain)
BRERA (Italy)
BRUNEI (Borneo)
BUCKINGHAM (England)
CA D'ORO (Italy)
CHAILLOT (France)
CHAMBORD (France)
CORFU (Greece)
CZERNIN (Czechoslovakia)
DOGES (Italy)
ELYSEE (France)
FARNESE (Italy)
FONTAINEBLEAU (France)
HAMPTON COURT (England)
HOLYROOD (Scotland)
KARLSKIRCHE (Austria)
KENSINGTON (England)
LA GRANJA (Spain)
LUXEMBOURG (France)
PITTI (Italy)
ROYAL (Monaco)
SCHONBRUNN (Austria)
STROZZI (Italy)
TESSIN (Sweden)
UFFIZI (Italy)
VERSAILLES (France)
WALDSTEIN (Czechoslovakia)

```
L K F C H A I L L O T K I R
N C Z A U F F I Z I A Z A E
T O Y D R O P C O R F Z T E
O R R O Q N S I L L A Q B T
L F U R R T E S T C J N R B
K U O O R A K S L T I Z U O
E S X O C I J A E E I C N S
N C Z E R N I N T A K Z E C
S Z C C M E O S A I R L I H
I T H Q J B D T N R L E O O
N E A E E L O G P I G L R N
G S M R A E H U A M Y A B B
T S B W E A S S R R A S L R
O I O A M U R Y O G E H E U
N N R N Z E B O L A Y O R N
O N D S V A D O G E S Q Z N
```

The solution is on page 87.

CASTLE CONVENTION

Although less plush than palaces, castles were the homes of many British aristocrats during medieval times. We've lowered the drawbridge to reveal 34 of these fortified dwellings for you to tour and circle.

ACRE

ALNWICK

ARUNDEL

BODIAM

CAWDOR

CHIRK

CORFE

CRATHES

CULZEAN

DEAL

DOVER

DUNROBIN

DUNVEGAN

DURHAM

EASTNOR

GLAMIS

HARLECH

HEVER

HOD HILL

LEEDS

LINCOLN

LUDLOW

MAIDEN

MIDDLEHAM

NORHAM

NUNNEY

ORFORD

POWIS

RAGLAN

THREAVE

WARDOUR

WARKWORTH

WINDSOR

YORK

```
E K R I H C R A T H E S B D
A V H C E L R A H G I F U O
S M A H E L D D I M D N S R
T C A E B O D I A M V I L F
N H D I R K P L N E W J E O
O S R E D H G W G O N D D R
R G R F M E T A P H L G N D
C C L R D U N R O B I N U R
A Y R O L A E D O V E R R O
W E A C E V H O K W H M A S
D N G Z E I T U F A K T W D
O N L H L O V R M A H R O N
R U A L N W I C K R O Y A I
C N N L O C N I L U D L O W
```

The solution is on page 87.

BEHIND THE SCENES

"LIGHTS! CAMERA! ACTION!" yells the DIRECTOR, and another story is acted out and recorded on film. This has been going on since 1903, when the first moving picture with a plot, *The Great Train Robbery*, was produced. Other moviemaking terms you're likely to hear behind the scenes make up the SCRIPT for this puzzle.

```
P R O T C E R I D F O C U S
R A N B L E S T H G I L U T
O F E F S N N O I T A C O L
P A E I E E U L L I T S C T
E D R L K C S A R T X E O U
R E C M T S C R I P T F S O
T I S C R E E N P L A Y T E
Y N C O G S Q R P R K U U D
A U T S A C I U E D A L M A
M C G W T N E M P I U Q E F
A S T S T S A T M A K E U P
R T J I O C N A Z L T F S M
O U I L O U T L L O R R T U
N D C L T N N I J G O A A S
A I Q S T U C D D U K M R I
P O I N S P L I C E W E R C
```

The solution is on page 87.

ACTION
ACTORS
CAMERA
CAST
CLOSE-UP
COSTUME
CREW
CUT
DIALOGUE
DIRECTOR
EDIT
EQUIPMENT
EXTRAS
FADE-IN
FADE-OUT
FILM
FOCUS
FRAME
LENS
LIGHTS
LOCATION
MAKEUP
MUSIC
PANORAMA
PRINT
PROPERTY
ROLL
SCENE
SCREEN
SCREENPLAY
SCRIPT
SET
SOUND
SPLICE
STAR
STILL
STUDIO
STUNT
TAKE
ZOOM

RAVISHING RUGS

The art of carpet weaving reached its peak early in the 16th century in the mountainous regions of Turkey, Persia and China, where the fleece of sheep and the hair of camels and goats grow fine and long. This time-consuming trade has produced beautiful oriental rug styles, some of which are listed below.

ABADEH
AFSHAR
ALTAI
BALUCHI
BIJAR
BOKHARA
BOTEH
DHURRI
DORUYE
HERATI
HERIZ
ISFAHAN
KASHGAI
KELIM
MAMLUK
MESHED
MILAS
MIR
MORI
MUD
NAIN
PALAS
POLONAISE
QUM
SAMARKAND
SAPH
SARUK
SERABAND

SERAPI
SINKIANG
TABRIZ

USHAK
VEREMIN
YALLAHMEH

```
A L O P N S A M A R K A N D
B O K H A R A I P A R E S N
A J T K H L J I S R I I L A
D P A Q A Z A H T H V J M B
E O B I F Z G S C A E B O A
H L R K S A R U K Z R T T R
P O I U I A L T A I E E R E
M N Z L Y A L L A H M E H S
Z A B M B E Q J F E I U M U
U I Z A X I N C S R N Q Q S
Q S X M N Q J H H I Q J A A
I E H A U Q E A A Z B L S P
J K I A Q D H U R R I T P H
G N A I K N I S Q M I L E K
```

The solution is on page 87.

"CAR"-MEN

Abraham LINCOLN, as a lawyer for the Rock Island Railroad, defended the right to build the first bridge across the Mississippi River. George PULLMAN, after an uncomfortable overnight journey by train, invented the first comfortable sleeping car. From LINCOLN to PULLMAN and beyond, here are people who have had a hand in keeping America's trains chugging along.

ALLEN (Horatio)
AMES (Oakes)
ANDREWS (James)
BALDWIN (Matthias)
BLAIR (John)

BRADY (Matthew)
BRAGG (Braxton)
BRICE (Calvin)
COFFIN (Lorenzo)
COOPER (Peter)

CROCKER (Charles)
DEBS (Eugene V.)
DREW (Daniel)
FISK (James)
FLAGLER (Henry)
FULLER (W. A.)
GRANT (Ulysses S.)
HANCOCK (Winfield)
HAUPT (Herman)
HENRY (John)
HILL (James)
JANNEY (Eli H.)
JONES (Casey)
KING (William)
LEE (Robert E.)
LINCOLN (Abraham)
McKEEN (W. R.)
MINOT (Charles)
PULLMAN (George)
RENO (Brothers)
ROOT (James)
SHAY (Ephraim)
SHELLEY (Kate)
ULRICH (J. H.)
WATSON (T. B.)
WATT (James)
WEBB (Sim)
WESTINGHOUSE (George)
WHALON (C. M.)
WINANS (Ross)

```
F U L L E R S W E R D N A N
I L S W H A L O N C I O M W
S I A M I N O T M O W M E Y
K N E G L Q E C G F A S S E
H C I R L U K O R F T T C L
A O J R D E B S A I S O A L
N L A E E B R H N N O O C E
C N N N E L A G T P N R I H
O A N O J U H L E T O I E S
C M E L P O S R D C A N B D
K L Y T U H N W K W R W L R
I L Y S A L L E N Y I M A E
N U E Y D A R B S N A N I W
G P I E C I R B O G G A R B
```

The solution is on page 87.

58

RARE "CAR"-TEL

Studebaker, Edsel and Packard were once familiar names to the American car-buying public. How many of these other models of the '50s can you recognize?

ARNOLT

ASARDO

ASCOT

ASTRA-GNOME

BOCAR

BUCKBOARD

CHECKER

CHEETAH

CHICAGOAN

CROFTON

CUSTER

DARRIN

DAYTONA

DEVIN

EDWARDS

EL MOROCCO

GAYLORD

GRANTHAM

GREGORY

MANECO

MOSS

MOTA

MUNTZ

PANDA

PIONEER

POWELL

ROGUE

SCARAB

SKORPION

STAR DUST

STORM

VICTRESS

YANK

```
B I L J Y T R R E K C E H C
A G U L M K E L Z T N U M N
R I V R E T E F D P C A I Y
A T O M S W N R E Q H V M X
C T D U P R O H A T E E H C
S J C A D L I P N D H E S H
D T N S Y A P A R K Y L S I
R D A A S T R A G N O M E C
A L G R E G O R Y A E O R A
W R H D D B K N I Y U R T G
D P A O K U S O A N G O C O
E T O C S A S L Z L O C I A
J Y U W O N O T F O R C V N
K B N A I B M A N E C O A B
```

The solution is on page 87.

IRIS INFATUATION

"In myth, legend and religion, in heraldry, tapestries and the robes of kings, in magic, medicine and botany, irises have appeared since the dawn of recorded history," observed flower expert Molly Price. Below we've gathered a variety of these beautiful perennials that are easy to grow and come in all colors of the rainbow.

AGATHA
AHOY
AMAS
AMIGO

ANKARA
ARCADY
ARCTIC BLUE
ARTEMIS

BANG
BARIA
BLACK ONYX
BLUE CAPE
BOCENA
BRAVADO
CARMELA
CLAIRE
CLARA
CURTSY
DAYSTAR
ELVIRA
GAUCHO
ISOLDA
KAHILI
LADY KAY
LUCIA
LUNA
MAGNET
NANA
OBERON
ORESTES
PAGODA
PEE WEE
PSYCHE
RANGER
ROBBY
SABLE
TROPHY
VERA

```
C L A I R E S O D A V A R B
A D L O S I T A H R R Q K N
R R R A M I G O H C C A A N
M B E E H A K B A T H N O B
E A T V G O R D O I A R R B
L R S W Y N Y I L C E G A L
A I N E S F A I V B E I A A
D A Y S T A R R O L C N R C
O P B L R S A M A U E A A K
G S B X U J E D L E L M R O
A Y O A C N Y R W C B P A N
P C R D N K A E O A A V K Y
O H C U A G E R L P S Z N X
Y E D Y H P O R T E N G A M
```

The solution is on page 87.

A ZEAL FOR ZINNIAS

Zinnias capture the essence of summer and make a showy splash of radiant color in anyone's garden. The versatile flowers come in many sizes and, depending upon the kind, have quilled, ruffly or curled petals. Create your own BOUQUET of zinnia types by circling the words here.

BIG RED

BIG TOP

BLAZE

BOUQUET

BUTTON

CLASSIC

CORAL

DASHER

ENVY

EXQUISITE

FLAME

GODDESS

GOLD SUN

IVORY

LILLIPUT

LOLLIPOP

PETER PAN

PINWHEEL

POLAR BEAR

POMPON

PRINCE

PULCINO

PURITY

QUEEN

RED MAN

RUFFLES

SNOWMAN

SPLENDOR

SUNSHINE

TORCH

ZENITH

```
S B U T T O N A P R E T E P
L N G N T E U Q U O B I M L
I S O V A D P F E D M V A Y
L S L W J M F P E N N O L P
L E D X M L D X U E V R F O
I D S D E A Q E E L H Y D P
P D U S A U N U R P C E Z I
U O N C I S Q N B S R I E L
T G T S I Y H L O G O L N L
F N I G T S A E I P T A I O
B T R I I Z S B R W M R T L
E K R A E B R A L O P O H C
S U N S H I N E L Q H C P T
P I N W H E E L E C N I R P
```

The solution is on page 88.

61

ADAM'S RIB

According to Genesis, God looked at Adam and said, "It is not good that the man should be alone; I will make a helpmate for him." So He took a rib from Adam and created EVE, the first woman. From DELILAH, who betrayed Samson, to MARY, mother of Jesus, many prominent biblical women are named in the list below.

ABIGAIL
ADAH
ANAH
ANNA

BATHSHEBA
BERNICE
CANDACE
CHLOE

CLAUDIA
DEBORAH
DELILAH
DINAH
DORCAS
DRUSILLA
ELIZABETH
ESTHER
EUNICE
EVE
HAGAR
HANNAH
HULDAH
LEAH
LOIS
LYDIA
MARA
MARTHA
MARY
MERAB
NAOMI
PERSIS
PHOEBE
PUAH
RACHEL
REBEKAH
RHODA
RUTH
SARAH
SERAH
TIMNA

```
B E C A L H U L D A H A U P
A O L E I R E B E K A H M A
R L A N M I T E R H G B H D
E H U E S A C R O D A T T O
M C D C H A R E S T R I E H
M M I I D N U Y H A H H B R
D O A N I A T S M A R A A S
M E A U R H H L R I E N Z T
E C L E D E L O I S N N I A
B A B I B V B A D A H A L L
E R N A L E H C A R G H E Y
O A G Z D A I M O A N I A D
H M I E S T H E R H B G B I
P E R S I S D R U S I L L A
```

The solution is on page 88.

SPREADING THE WORD

The disciples of Jesus traveled extensively after his death, spreading his teachings throughout the Mediterranean lands and even into Asia. The 29 places they visited can be found in the Acts of the Apostles in the Bible as well as in this word list.

ANTIOCH

ASIA

BITHYNIA

CAESAREA

CILICIA

CORINTH

CRETE

CYPRUS

CYRENE

DAMASCUS

EPHESUS

GALATIA

GALILEE

JERUSALEM

JOPPA

JUDAEA

LIBYA

MILETUS

OLIVET (Mt.)

PAPHOS

RHODES

ROME

SALAMIS

SAMARIA

SAMOS

SIDON

SYRIA

TARSUS

TYRE

```
C M I L E T U S L A S O M A S
A C E G A J R G E T Y D B I E
N R O L V S L R A G R A N T H
T J O Z A U A P O L I V E T A
I D A M A S C U S S A R L E P
O P T H E E U A M S C T A I P
C A U A I H I R U V S D I C O
H I C O R P T R E A U E S A J
P N L N J E P N M J E N A S L
H Y R I M Y T A I L Y E S I I
C H M Q C I R A I R T R B D U
A T R O L I G L R E O Y T O N
E I V S A L A M I S A C R N E
R B Y E N G T S A J U D E E T
S E D O H R P A P H O S S Y R
```

The solution is on page 88.

FULL HOUSE

We think you'll be quite adept at solving this Full House of 56 terms. All the entries contain four or more letters; words within larger words are not included. Once you're DONE, every letter will have been looped at least once.

ACED
ALTERATION
ARCED
AXLE
BALANCED

BILE
BLISS
BOND
BOTCH
BRAND

BREAK
BREEZE
BUZZING
CAMERA
CANTER

CHANGED
CHARD
COMA
CORAL
CREWEL

CRONY
DONE
EVEN
FEEL
GAZEBO
HERO
IMBUE
INDEED
INDEX
INKED
IRONY
MANUAL
MAUL
MAXIMS
MELODY
MINCE
MOMENTARY
MORE
NAIVE
NODE
PARADE
PERIL
RALLIED
RARE
RECEDED
RISK
SHARPER
SOLVE
STAR
TARE
TENANT
TOPICAL
TRACE
TRILL
WEBBED
ZENITH

```
M A N U A L T E R A T I O N
C O R A L L I E D E N M A Y
C A M E R A R I S K T I D N
B R E E Z E O H E A V N R O
U C L R N I N D E E D C A R
Z E O O D T Y R E R N E H C
Z D D M N G A Z E B O T C H
I E Y A A T E R E C B X R A
N F N X R U R V Y V E E E N
G E L I B A L A N C E D W G
T E L M T O P I C A L N E E
B L I S S H A R P E R I L D
```

The solution is on page 88.

FULL HOUSE

Here's another Full House puzzle, with a FRESH assortment of words. Can you SPEAR all 48 terms? You'll know if the puzzle has been solved successfully when each letter has been circled at least once.

ANNUL
AVER
BOILED
BRONZE
BURDEN
CAKE
CEREAL
CHECK
CHIC
CRAWLED
DIAPERS
EVIDENT
FAME
FIGHT
FRESH
GERBIL
GLAZED
GOAT
GORE
GRAY
HEREBY
INQUIRING
INSTANCE
LEDGER
MILK
NORMAL
PALS
PIXIES

PLANK
RANI
RAZZ
REALISM
REDUCTION

REHASH
SAGA
SHALE
SHOWY
SPEAR

TENOR
TERROR
TOMORROW
UNIT
WEARY

WHARF
WIZARD
WREN
ZITI
ZOOM

```
G P I X I E S H O W Y B R T
P L A N K D E L I O B U E A
R E A L I S M Z W R E R D O
E W I Z S H A L E R R D U G
G M H S E R F U A O E E C N
D B M A D D L N R M H N T I
E R O G R L I N Y O R N I R
L O O A A F B A K T E O O I
W N Z E E I R C P D Z N N U
A Z R K P G E E I E E I N Q
R E H A S H G V V T R I T N
C I H C C T E C N A T S N I
```

The solution is on page 88.

MAPMAKER, MAPMAKER

The modern system of mapmaking grew from the charts of the ancient Greeks and was changed very little until the 16th century, when printing techniques were developed and explorers discovered new lands. Here you'll find the names of several people who've charted their way into history books with their mapmaking abilities.

ABBOT (H. L.)
ABERT (J. J.)
ADAMS (John)

BELLIN (Jacques Nicolas)
BIEN (Julius)

BLOME (Richard)
BOWEN (Emanuel)
BOWLES (John)
BRAUN (Georg)
BUELL (Abel)
CAMDEN (William)
CAREY (Matthew)
DUDLEY (Sir Robert)
FADEN (William)
FOSTER (John)
GREUTER (Matthew)
KITCHEN (Thomas)
LAURIE (Robert)
MOLL (Herman)
MORDEN (Robert)
MOULE (Thomas)
MOUNT (Richard)
NORDEN (John)
PETTY (Sir William)
SAXTON (Christopher)
SAYER (Robert)
SELLER (John)
SENEX (John)
SMITH (Captain John)
SPEED (John)

```
C T N U O M K N U A R B
M O L L A U R I E Q S D
Z B S Z L K T M Q J M U
O B Y A N E M O L B A D
C A R E Y O Y U B Z D L
K L D F R E L L E S A E
D A Z D R L R E K M V Y
F N E I B E F I Y I T E
X N G R E U T E R T K B
B E Z A Z C M S E H O E
U D N B H J Q P O W J L
E R N E D M A C L F C L
L O N R S C N E W O B I
L N O T X A S P E E D N
```

The solution is on page 88.

ANGLESEARCH: SAY IT!

In this Anglesearch, all the entries are words that mean "say." Remember, each word forms an angle, and no two words cross each other.

```
T A H B L F C O N V P R A T
O X C A L K S T A E E T A T
V D A T H G R T L R W C R L
I W D E C L E Z X S Y V P E
S V K A E A I N F E T T A T
E Z T J P R T I O Z L A L B
Y X U T S E O T R J E B J G
S P O H N N H N M S S O G L
N F E R G G H E Q I F Z L E
O S L C I T E M M P K Z Z Y
C E H A E M B T C E L L L R
R V C E Y R U I J U Q E E Q
Z J Q L R R H N L T T P S B
B A B B E C G R E T S I H W
```

The solution is on page 88.

ADVISE
BABBLE
BLAB
CHAT
CHIN
CONFER
CONVERSE
DECLARE
GOSSIP
INFORM
LECTURE
~~MENTION~~
PRATE
PRATTLE
RECITE
RELAY
SPEAK
SPOUT
STATE
TALK
TATTLE
TELL
UTTER
WHISPER
YELL

WINE . . .

One of the largest wine cellars in the world is in the Cienaga Winery of the Almaden Vineyards in Hollister, California. This large plant, which covers 4 acres, can house 37,300 oak barrels containing 1.83 million gallons of different wines.

ANGELICA

BACO NOIR

BARBERA

BURGUNDY

CATAWBA

CHABLIS

CHAMPAGNE

CHARDONNAY

CHENIN BLANC

CHIANTI

CLARET

CONCORD

DELAWARE

GAMAY

MADEIRA

MARSALA

MOSELLE

MUSCATEL

NIAGARA

PINOT BLANC

PINOT NOIR

PORT

RHINE

RIESLING

ROSE

SAUTERNE

SEMILLON

SHERRY

SYLVANER

TOKAY

TRAMINER

VERMOUTH

ZINFANDEL

```
Y M A B W A T A C I L E G N A
E A C P B L S A U T E R N E R
R R N I D A B A C O N O I R A
A S A N R M U S C A T E L N G
W A L O O E L L E S O M S R A
A L B T C D N C Y C G Y E I I
L A N B N T R A H D A R I O N
E R I L O R K A V C M R R N O
D I N A C O M E H L A E O T L
N E E N T P R A E C Y H S O L
A D H C A M B B L A L S E N I
F A C G O L A R E B R A B I M
N M N U I C H I A N T I R P E
I E T S Y D N U G R U B N E S
Z H C E N I H R E N I M A R T
```

The solution is on page 88.

...AND CHEESE

Did you know that the most prodigious cheese eaters are the people of France? According to statistics, the French have an annual cheese consumption of 43 pounds per person. And they don't have to worry about supplies running out—the United States, the largest cheese producer in the world, produces 4,773,500,000 pounds a year!

BEL PAESE

BLUE

BRICK

BRIE

CAMEMBERT

CHEDDAR

CHESHIRE

COLBY

COTTAGE

CREAM

EDAM

FETA

GORGONZOLA

GOUDA

GRUYERE

JACK

LIEDERKRANZ

LIMBURGER

MONTEREY

MOZZARELLA

MUENSTER

NEUFCHATEL

PARMESAN

PETIT SUISSE

PORT DU SALUT

PROVOLONE

RICOTTA

ROMANO

ROQUEFORT

SAMSOE

SAPSAGO

STILTON

SWISS

```
E D Q M N O T L I T S S I W S
Z T R O F E U Q O R I C O T A
N A M Z O R I C O T T A G E M
A L O Z N O G R O G A S P A S
R L N A T C H E S H I R E T O
K E T R G U D A Y E E E I L E
R T E E O O L M P R I L I E E
E A R L T K U A A E R M U K N
D H E L C E R D S Y B L O C O
E C Y A N M D E A U B O K I L
I F J S E E A U R R D D C R O
L U T S H P F G O G O T O B V
O E A C L E E O N A M O R O O
R N O E T R E B M E M A C O R
E Y B A E S S I U S T I T E P
```

The solution is on page 88.

FLOATING MANSIONS

The perfection of the marine steam engine made the late 19th and early 20th centuries the golden age of yachting. European royalty and American millionaires went to sea in floating mansions fitted with crystal chandeliers, tapestry walls and ornate furnishings. Some seagoing showplaces of that period are docked in the diagram.

ALVA
ARA
ARIES

BRITANNIA
CORSAIR
DAPHNE

DEERHOUND
DJINN
DRYAD
ENDYMION
ERIN
FALCON
FANCY
FANTASIA
FINLANDIA
GANYMEDE
GREIF
HAWKE
INGOMAR
JEFFERSON
LYNDONIA
MARGARITA
MARY
MIRAMAR
NOMA
NOURMAHAL
ONEIDA
ORION
SEA CLOUD
TARANTULA
WATERWITCH
YANKEE
ZAIDA

```
Y A I D N A L N I F A N C Y
C D L I C O R S A I R E K J
S I R H C T I W R E T A W A
E E O A M O N M Y R A M V A
A N E R M K O H Y G R L G I
C O K I Z A I D A D A A W S
L D W E L B R I T A N N I A
O J A S E I O I R Y T E M T
U I H P L A H A M R U O N N
D N U O H R E E D D L G O A
C N O L Y N D O N I A C H F
E Y A N K E E C O X L Y E O
A I N G O M A R G A R I T A
W H N O S R E F F E J B O E
```

The solution is on page 89.

WATER WORKS

"It FLOWs down, clear and cool from the heights of Hermon; it gathers in its riches that it may POUR them out again to fertilize Jordan," wrote Harry Emerson Fosdick about the Sea of Galilee. We've added some other things water can do in the list below.

BOIL
BUBBLE
CASCADE
DRENCH
DRIP
DRIZZLE
EBB
EDDY
FALL
FLOOD
FLOW
FOAM
FROTH
GUSH
JET
OOZE
POUR
RAIN
RIPPLE
RISE
SEEP
SHOWER
SLOSH
SOAK
SPATTER
SPLASH
SPLATTER
SPOUT

SPRAY
SPRINKLE
SPURT

SQUIRT
SURGE
TRICKLE

```
L F E L B B U B R V H C
O E L P P I R E O X S W
Z A K O R Y T S Z I A K
F L N A O T R I C K L E
R F I F A D I R Y H P L
C N R L T R U P S D S A
H A P O J V Q J R S D E
E S S W T S S E E P Z E
L G J C H H N S L O S H
Z M R O A C R Y O U T F
Z T W U H D A U Q T O B
I E E S S R E S O A K E
R A U J P I Z Y M P J B
D G L S S P A T T E R B
```

The solution is on page 89.

71

ROLLING RIVERS

Trace the romance, beauty and history of Western Europe by hunting for Strauss' beautiful blue DANUBE and other famous rivers that meander within the banks of this Word Search diagram.

DANUBE
DNEPR
DNESTR
DOURO

DRINA
DVINA
EBRO
ELBE

GUADIANA
KEMIJOKI
LAGEN
LOIRE
MARITSA
MARNE
MENDERES
MORAVA
MUONIO
MURESUL
ODER
ONEGA
OTTERAEN
PRIPYAT
RHINE
RHONE
SAONE
SEINE
SOMME
TAJO
TANAELV
TEVERE
TULOMA
VARDAR
VIENNE
VISTULA
WARTA
WESER

```
A S T I R A M E N D E R E S
O E W H O T T E R A E N H A
V I O V C D N S J I E B R O
L N N Q D I E C O G O F L N
E E J O H W X R A M W L G E
A Q W R U D A L Q N M V U J
N V H K E M I J O K I E A Q
A O A M O M U R E S U L D H
T Q R L T A Y P I R P V I R
E A U U U J W Z X T I W A T
V T G Q O T E B U N A D N S
E R P E N D S W A R R J A E
R V I E N N E I T A W Q O N
E N R A M O R A V A N I R D
```

The solution is on page 89.

TOWERING TREES

Many people have taken measures to protect the environment from further harm by reducing their trash, preserving wildlife habitats and recycling paper. Another way to help save Mother Earth is to plant trees, which help mankind survive by photosynthesizing carbon monoxide into oxygen.

APPLE
ASH
BALSA
BAY
BEECH
BIRCH
CATALPA
CEDAR
CHERRY
CHESTNUT
CORK
COTTONWOOD
CYPRESS
DOGWOOD
EBONY
ELDER
ELM
EUCALYPTUS
FIR
HEMLOCK
HICKORY
HOLLY
JUNIPER
LARCH
LAUREL
LEMON
LIME
MAGNOLIA
MAHOGANY
MAPLE
MULBERRY
OAK
ORANGE
PEACH
PEAR
PINE

PLUM
POPLAR
REDWOOD
SEQUOIA
SPRUCE

SYCAMORE
TEAK
WALNUT
WILLOW
YEW

```
C Y P R E S S D B K C Y T J
E A P D U F E B O C R G U U
E B T E C F Q I A O H R N N
C C O A A I U R K L W A T I
O E U N L R O C O M L D S P
T L J R Y P I H R E I E E E
T D B K P H A L A H M C H R
O E A A T S E L N P E A C H
N R L P U Y N A G O H A M C
W M S P S C I U E N C K A H
O Q A L A A P R W R R R G E
O K A E T M W E Y O A M N R
D O G W O O D L C L L U O R
M U L B E R R Y P H O L L Y
L H S A L E M O N S P P I V
E B E E C H P Z T U N L A W
```

The solution is on page 89.

73

HIDDEN NUMBERS

The number combinations in the list are hidden in the diagram horizontally, vertically, or diagonally in a straight, unbroken line of digits that reads forward or backward.

```
0  8  7  7  8  9  2  1  4  6  7
7  4  8  7  9  3  9  3  9  5  7
9  5  9  9  9  7  4  4  4  9  4
1  7  2  5  6  0  9  7  8  5  3
2  6  2  1  7  9  8  2  6  0  9
6  2  1  4  9  8  0  1  9  5  4
4  3  6  7  4  9  6  8  3  7  6
8  3  8  7  5  7  9  6  0  8  3
7  9  6  8  5  1  5  1  8  3  6
0  4  8  1  6  7  3  4  4  9  6
7  5  7  0  9  8  2  4  8  6  1
```

0757	2298
0784	2345
0877	2359
0898	3084
0969	3098
0978	3344
1467	3394
1498	3946
1576	3978
1586	4376
1679	4449
1684	4556
2186	4591
2197	4869
2267	4999

The solution is on page 89.

HIDDEN NUMBERS

To multiply your pleasure, we offer another group of numbers to be circled. They add up to a rewarding Search, so give them your undivided attention, and let nothing subtract from your success.

```
2 8 0 4 8 4 3 6 2 3 3
2 1 2 3 5 0 4 5 2 5 9
1 6 1 4 5 5 4 0 1 1 0
9 8 2 5 4 9 9 3 5 4 4
4 3 5 1 3 5 4 5 4 7 7
1 3 4 2 1 8 2 2 3 5 1
7 2 0 3 4 0 3 0 5 7 3
8 4 4 6 9 3 1 0 2 0 0
2 4 8 3 5 2 3 6 5 5 3
3 5 5 3 2 3 7 4 4 0 9
5 0 0 1 0 1 7 6 0 1 0
```

The solution is on page 89.

5035	7454
5123	7503
5209	7550
5236	8032
5322	8043
5405	8235
6010	8244
6034	8404
6101	8451
6145	9122
6214	9155
6233	9303
7323	9350
7355	9504
7450	9513

The **27** things on wheels in the Word List are hidden horizontally, vertically or diagonally on all three faces of the cube-shaped diagram. A word may be entirely hidden on one face of the cube, or it may start on one face and bend onto a second or third. When a word begins diagonally on one face of the cube, it will continue on a diagonal if it bends onto an adjoining face. **SKATEBOARD** is circled to start you off.

AUTO
BICYCLE
BUS
CARRIAGE
COMBINE
DOLLY
FORKLIFT
GO-CART
GOLF CART

MOPED
MOTORCYCLE
MOWER
ROLLER SKATE
SHOPPING CART
SKATEBOARD
SNOW BLOWER
SNOWPLOW
STROLLER

TRACTOR
TRAILER
TRAIN
TRICYCLE
TROLLEY
TRUCK
UNICYCLE
WAGON
WHEELBARROW

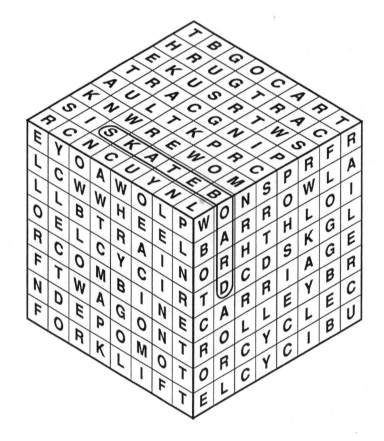

The solution is on page 90.

LOOSE LETTERS

To solve this multi-part challenger, first remove one letter from each six-letter word in the list to form a new five-letter word (do not change the order of the letters); write the "removed" letter in the blank provided. Then look for the new word in the diagram below. The "loose" letters, when read down, will reveal a proverb. We did the first one to get you started.

WORD	REMOVED LETTER
1. PLIANT	I
2. GRINDS	—
3. GROVEL	—
4. EQUIPS	—
5. FENDED	—
6. FOAMED	—
7. SHOVEL	—
8. PACKED	—
9. SPRINT	—
10. THRASH	—
11. FORAGE	—
12. INVERT	—
13. BEACON	—
14. BASTES	—
15. THREAT	—
16. BEAKER	—
17. ELATER	—
18. WEAKEN	—
19. ASPIRE	—
20. GASPED	—
21. TRAVEL	—
22. SALUTE	—
23. SWEATS	—
24. IDEALS	—
25. SOUGHT	—
26. FOURTH	—
27. PRAYER	—
28. SCREAM	—

```
P  B  S  W  A  T  S  M  H  T  R  E  A  T
E  L  S  J  G  A  P  E  D  Q  P  G  S  R
B  T  A  Q  S  P  I  U  Q  H  S  R  C  E
A  A  U  N  S  H  R  M  T  R  C  O  Z  N
C  T  I  A  T  H  E  R  W  S  R  F  Z  I
O  R  R  T  S  Z  O  N  A  B  A  C  O  N
G  R  O  V  E  F  D  V  K  M  M  T  L  S
R  R  F  R  R  T  D  M  E  L  H  K  E  L
V  E  T  E  N  D  E  D  N  G  S  S  V  A
V  Y  K  H  Z  S  C  J  U  Z  A  G  A  E
E  A  T  E  R  U  A  O  T  B  R  H  R  D
B  P  Z  R  Y  E  P  R  I  N  T  G  U  O
```

The solution is on page 89.
Word list and proverb are on page 91.

LANGUAGE LESSON

Over 200 world languages are spoken by at least a million people. The following language lesson will help you become familiar with 42 of them.

AKAN (Ghana)
ARABIC
BATAK (Indonesia)
BEJA (Sudan)
BETI (Cameroon)
CATALAN (Spain)
CHIGA (Uganda)
CHINESE
CZECH
DANISH
DUTCH
EDO (Nigeria)
ENGLISH
FARSI (Iran)
FRENCH
GERMAN
GREEK
HEBREW
HINDI (India)
ITALIAN
JAPANESE
KAMBA (Kenya)
KOREAN
LAO (Laos)
LATVIAN
MAGYAR (Hungary)
MALAY (Indonesia)
MAORI
   (New Zealand)
MIN (Taiwan)
MORO (Philippines)
NEPALI
PORTUGUESE
RIFF (Morocco)
RUSSIAN

SHONA (Zimbabwe)
SPANISH
SWAHILI (Kenya)
THAI

URDU (Pakistan)
WOLOF (Senegal)
YORUBA (Benin)
ZULU (South Africa)

```
K A M B A T A K A N A M B O
P O T S B E T A R I Y A R P
Y R R U H S I N A P S O O N
O U R E J O H N B U M R C A
R D I T A X N A I L T I A F
U A F L P N E A C U D S O F
B N F N A M R E G Z O W E R
A I R Q N P R U S S I A N E
G S I T E B E M M A B H A N
I H L E S S O N A J E I I C
H D G R E E K F G L J L V H
C O N N I E D O Y L A I T C
E X I I N A I L A T I Y A T
Z H M T H A I O R I H S L U
C A T A L A N W E R B E H D
```

The solution is on page 89.

78

Answers

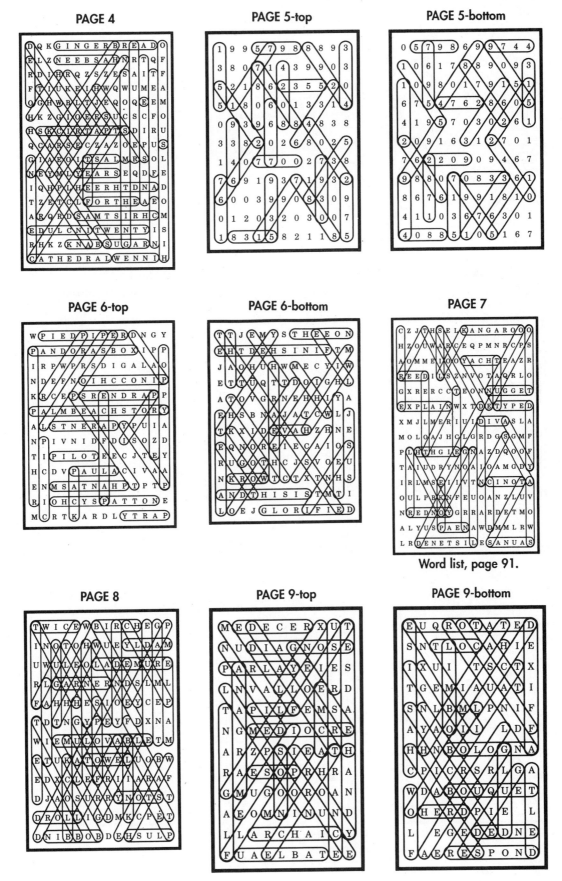

PAGE 4

PAGE 5-top

PAGE 5-bottom

PAGE 6-top

PAGE 6-bottom

PAGE 7

Word list, page 91.

PAGE 8

PAGE 9-top

PAGE 9-bottom

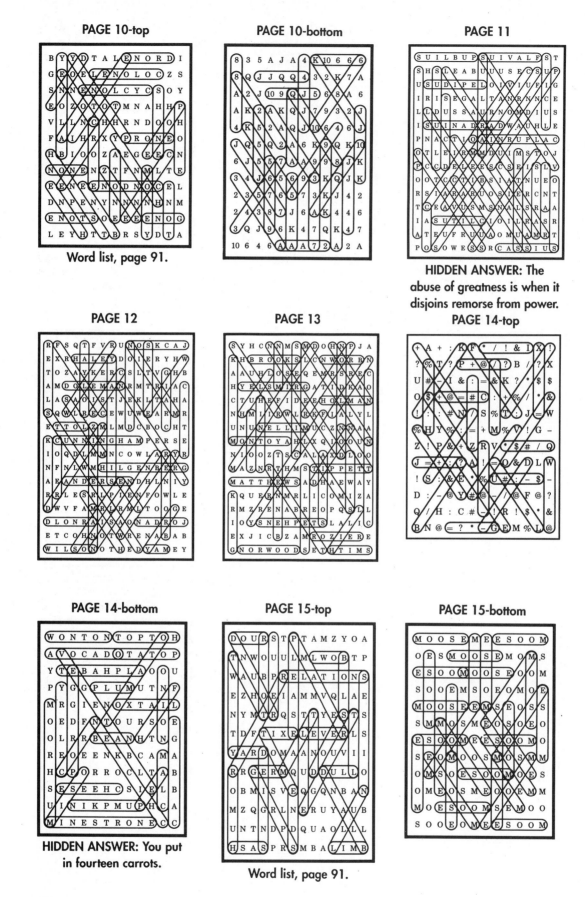

PAGE 10-top

Word list, page 91.

PAGE 10-bottom

PAGE 11

HIDDEN ANSWER: The abuse of greatness is when it disjoins remorse from power.

PAGE 12

PAGE 13

PAGE 14-top

PAGE 14-bottom

HIDDEN ANSWER: You put in fourteen carrots.

PAGE 15-top

Word list, page 91.

PAGE 15-bottom

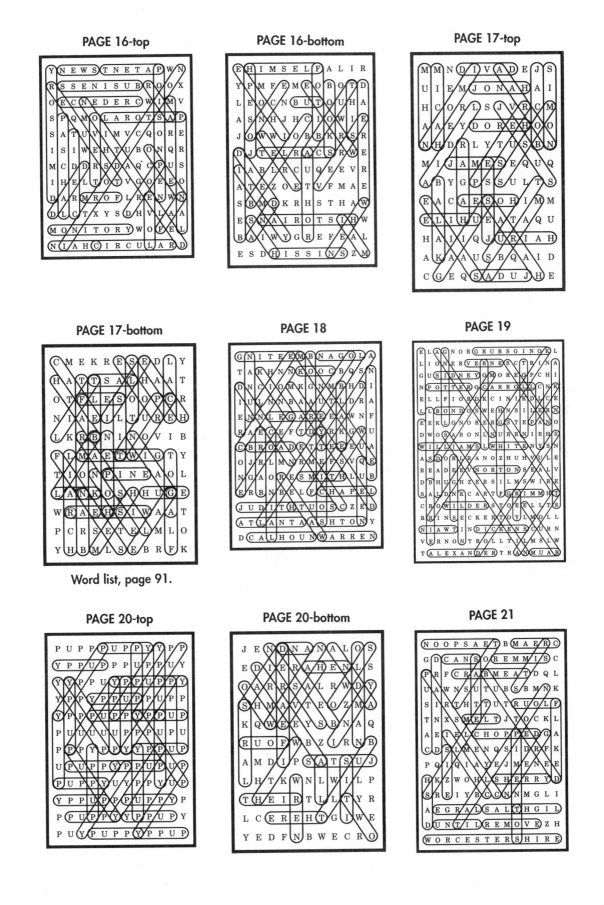

PAGE 16-top

PAGE 16-bottom

PAGE 17-top

PAGE 17-bottom

PAGE 18

PAGE 19

Word list, page 91.

PAGE 20-top

PAGE 20-bottom

PAGE 21

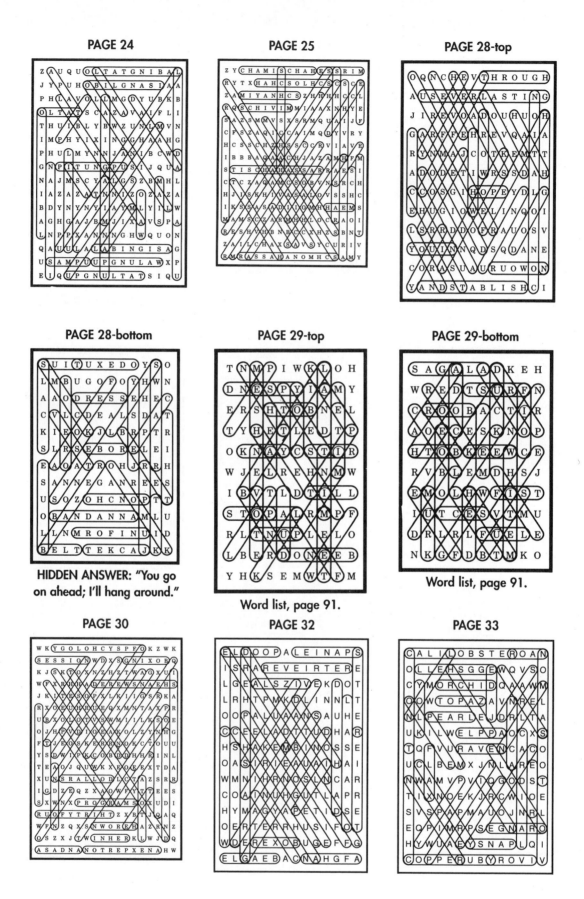

PAGE 24

PAGE 25

PAGE 28-top

PAGE 28-bottom

PAGE 29-top

PAGE 29-bottom

HIDDEN ANSWER: "You go on ahead; I'll hang around."

Word list, page 91.

Word list, page 91.

PAGE 30

PAGE 32

PAGE 33

PAGE 34

PAGE 35-top

PAGE 35-bottom

PAGE 36

PAGE 37

PAGE 38

PAGE 39

PAGE 40

PAGE 41

PAGE 42

PAGE 43

PAGE 45

PAGE 46

PAGE 47

PAGE 48

Cove-ring (Covering)

PAGE 49

PAGE 50

PAGE 51

Pen-knife (Penknife)

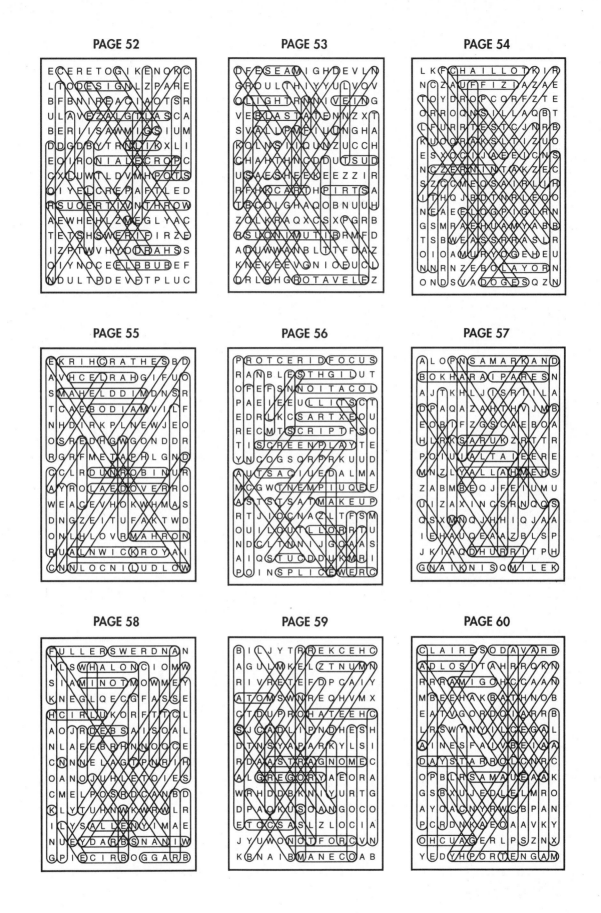

PAGE 52   PAGE 53   PAGE 54

PAGE 55   PAGE 56   PAGE 57

PAGE 58   PAGE 59   PAGE 60

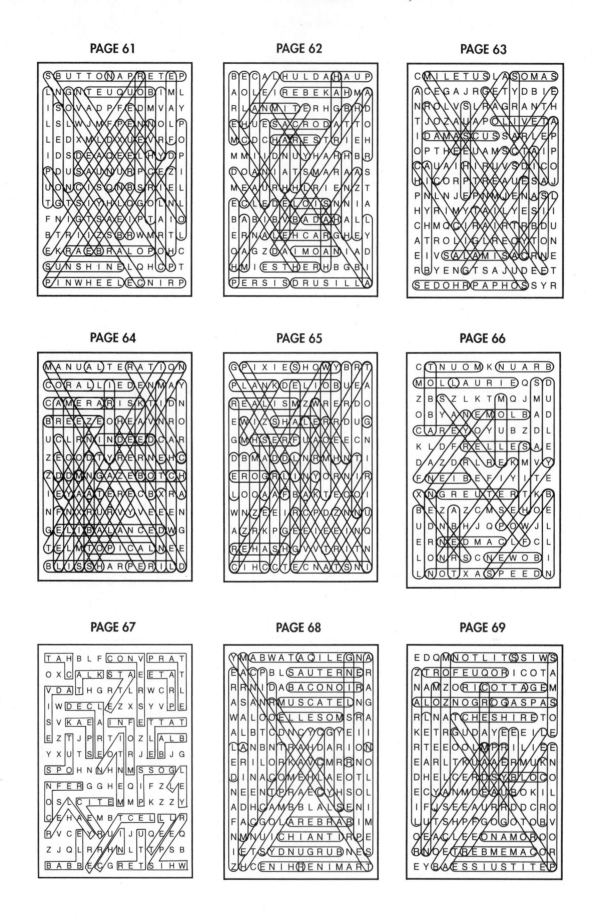

PAGE 61

PAGE 62

PAGE 63

PAGE 64

PAGE 65

PAGE 66

PAGE 67

PAGE 68

PAGE 69

88

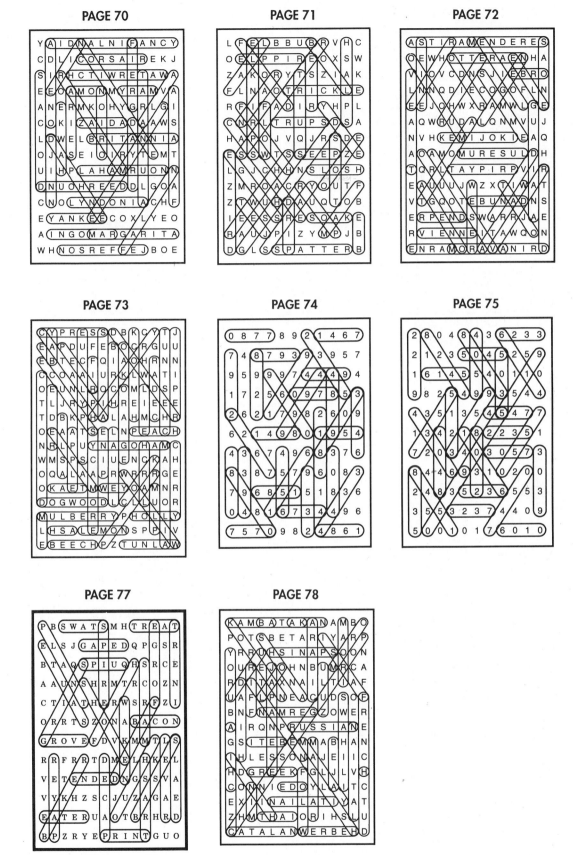

PAGE 70

PAGE 71

PAGE 72

PAGE 73

PAGE 74

PAGE 75

PAGE 77

PAGE 78

Word list, page 91.

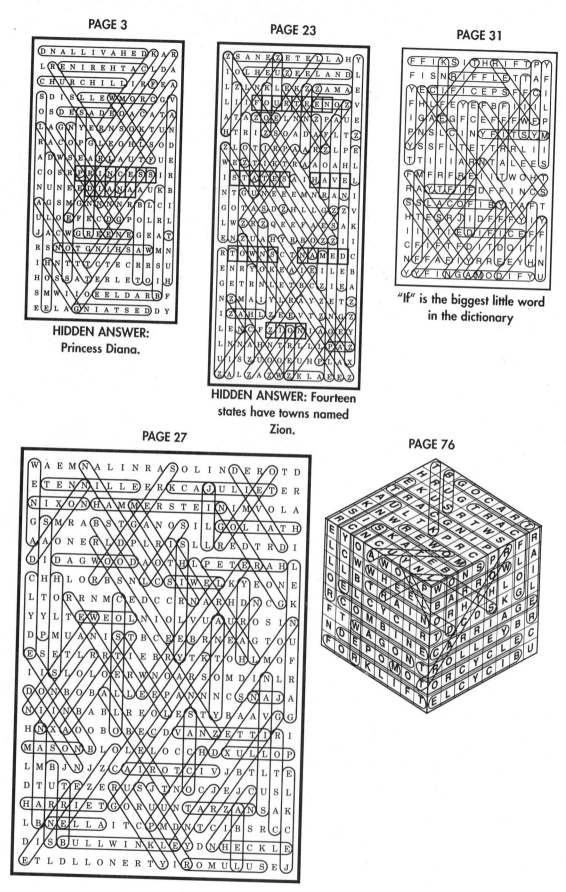

PAGE 3

HIDDEN ANSWER:
Princess Diana.

PAGE 23

HIDDEN ANSWER: Fourteen
states have towns named
Zion.

PAGE 31

"If" is the biggest little word
in the dictionary

PAGE 27

PAGE 76

WORD LIST FOR PAGE 7
TAIL TAG

Charge, explain, neat, tolled, deer, root, twist, twice, eighth, husky, yonder, rural, limbo, onion, natural, listened, dunking, govern, neap, poke, eyelid, donors, sail, lock, kangaroo, ocean, nugget, torso, opaque, envy, yacht, taut, typed, daffy, yoga, avid, drain, nods, soda, avows, saunas, smelt, tonic, card.

WORD LIST FOR PAGE 10-TOP
NUMBER "ONE" WORDS

Alone, atone, baloney, bone, clone, colonel, condone, cone, crone, cyclone, done, drone, gone, hone, honest, honey, intone, money, none, phone, phoney, pone, prone, shone, stone, throne, tone, zone.

WORD LIST FOR PAGE 15-TOP
TAIL TAG

Super, round, dour, robot, that, twenty, yard, deigns, sash, humor, rafter, relations, session, null, limb, bland, dull, lilt, trudge, equal, lever, revamp, please, exit, tome, ends, sprig, germ, malt, tend, does, slob, bowl.

WORD LIST FOR PAGE 17-BOTTOM
JACKPOT

Arch, bank, bath, belt, bran, café, crow, each, farm, fine, flag, gain, gale, hear, hope, huge, isle, lace, lank, last, lift, limb, lisp, mesh, nose, open, pine, punt, raft, rail (or liar), role, seen, self, slit, slot, spar (or raps), team, toga, twig, wish.

WORD LIST FOR PAGE 29-TOP
JACKPOT

Ably, beat, been, bond, both, chip, cloy, done, dual (or laud), espy, fell, flew, hard, heal, iota, item, land, lurk, meet (or teem), mesh, mint, mite, opal, oven, peak, pert, pint, poet, prim, punt, send, stir, stop (or pots), then, till, toil, toll, vote, yank.

WORD LIST FOR PAGE 29-BOTTOM
JACKPOT

Area, auto, beau, boor, both, coda, coif, cool, cove, dime, drip, duck, fist, flue, fuel, gala, grew, held, hood, item, leek (or keel), left, loud, mesa, murk, mush, nine, oboe, rock, rust, saga, sect, stub (or buts), surf, vise, week, whit.

WORD LIST FOR PAGE 77
LOOSE LETTERS

1. PLANT	I	6. FAMED	O	11. FORGE	A	17. EATER	L	23. SWATS	E
2. GRINS	D	7. SHOVE	L	12. INERT	V	18. WAKEN	E	24. DEALS	I
3. GROVE	L	8. PACED	K	13. BACON	E	19. SPIRE	A	25. OUGHT	S
4. QUIPS	E	9. PRINT	S	14. BASES	T	20. GAPED	S	26. FORTH	U
5. ENDED	F	10. TRASH	H	15. TREAT	H	21. RAVEL	T	27. PAYER	R
				16. BAKER	E	22. SAUTE	L	28. SCRAM	E

Proberb: Idle folks have the least leisure.